Editor
Janet Cain, M. Ed.

Managing Editor
Ina Massler Levin, M.A.

Editor-in-Chief
Sharon Coan, M.S. Ed.

Illustrator
Alexandra Artigas
Blanca Apodaca

Cover Artist
Brenda DiAntonis

Art Coordinator
Kevin Barnes

Art Director
CJae Froshay

Imaging
Alfred Lau
Ralph Olmedo, Jr.

Product Manager
Phil Garcia

Publishers
Rachelle Cracchiolo, M.S. Ed.
Mary Dupuy Smith, M.S. Ed.

Sing W[illegible]long

Recognize & Write Lowercase Letters

Authors

Ruth K. Baum
K. R. B. Arthur, M.S.

Teacher Created Materials

Teacher Created Materials, Inc.
6421 Industry Way
Westminster, CA 92683
www.teachercreated.com
ISBN-0-7439-3272-2

Table of Contents

Introduction

Sing Write Along is a level-headed and light-hearted approach to teaching lowercase traditional manuscript.

This book has been designed to provide a methodical progression of concepts and skills for teaching lowercase manuscript letters. It is comprehensive and is arranged to advance students from simple forms to the more complicated ones. The directions, which are provided as part of the text, are suitable for reading aloud to students and are appropriate for use by classroom teachers, as well as non-professionals. The children may be taught one-on-one or in small groups.

At the beginning of this book, there is a reproducible chart that allows teachers to keep a concise record of each child's progress. Use the chart to indicate mastery of the introductory skills, as well as the letters themselves.

Sections 1–5 of this book deal with letters of similar form and are divided into three parts: an introduction, the teaching of the letters themselves, and a review. Each introduction teaches concepts, which include the vocabulary and skills necessary for forming the letters to be taught in that lesson, and provides practice with those skills.

The middle part of each section introduces each family of letters, which are grouped by their similarities. The singing rhymes are used here, adding interest, reducing the situational tension of formal lessons, and reinforcing the directions for forming each letter. Children who write and sing at the same time find it nearly impossible to be stressed or tense and, therefore, learn more quickly and find the experience pleasurable.

The last part of each section is a review of both the newly taught letters and all the previously taught letters.

The rhymes for teaching the letters are printed separately so that they may be reproduced and used for classroom display.

In Section 6, Ghost Paper, which is a type of writing practice paper, is provided. Each ruled page is devoted to one letter shown in faint outline, making it suitable for tracing. These pages may be copied for any child who is not yet able to reproduce the letter forms. The Ghost Paper is bordered with pictures of items that begin with the letter being practiced. The pictures may be used to teach or reinforce initial letter sounds when appropriate.

In Section 7, there is a piece of Guide Paper and a Certificate of Completion, which may be reproduced for students. The Guide Paper is a ruled page of writing paper. The Certificate of Completion may be used to formally congratulate students when they have completed the course of study.

Section 1 of the program progresses at a very deliberate rate, providing a great deal of repetition and opportunity for success. Subsequent sections progress more rapidly as basic skills are mastered. To best meet the needs of each student, the lessons can easily be individualized by deleting pages or adding Ghost Paper pages.

Sing Write Along is a method that has not only been successful but has proven to be a relaxing and delightful experience for children. May its engaging presentation bring success to your writing program!

The Write Rhymes

Pages 4–8 contain all the rhymes that teach how to write the letters of the alphabet. It is suggested that you teach the rhymes shown below before you begin the program so students become familiar with the melody. The words may be sung to the tune of "Yankee Doodle" or "Jack and Jill," which are melodies many children already know. Teaching proper writing posture — feet flat on the floor; back comfortably touching the back of the chair; and arms on the desk, relaxed — go well with these rhymes. For an enlarged version of the rhymes below, see page 9.

When I write my ABC's,
I have an easy plan
I sit up straight and sing my song
And do the best I can.

Some letters are quite short and fat
And some of them are tall,
Some have stems and some have tails —
I try to write them all!

The Write Rhymes *(cont.)*

Use the following rhymes to teach circles, lines, and the letters **o**, **a**, **c**, **e**, **d**, and **b**. For enlarged versions of the rhymes below, see pages 36, 42, 56, and 61.

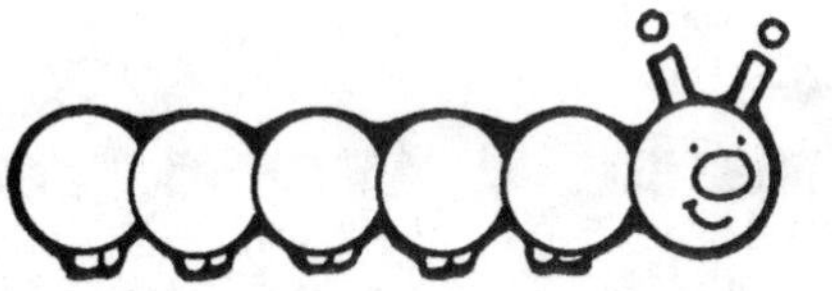

When I first begin to write,
I make a circle, so —
I make it round; I make it fat.
It is the letter o.

o and a and c and e,
I know I won't mistake them.
They don't stick up; they don't hang down
But sit right where I make them.

a and d are quite alike,
But I don't write the wrong one.
The stem on a is very short
And on the d a long one.

I never mix up d and b
Because it's very funny;
d looks like a silly duck,
And b looks like a bunny.

The Write Rhymes *(cont.)*

The rhymes on this page add dots and "tails" to the circles and lines and teach the letters **l**, **i**, **j**, **g**, **p**, and **q**. For an enlarged version of the rhymes below, see pages 89, 93, 98, and 103.

A long line downward from the top
I'm sure that you can tell,
This is an easy one to do.
It is the letter l.

Pull a line down, keep it straight,
Don't make it reach too high.
Then put a dot above its head,
It is the letter i.

You can change the letter i
In such a magic way,
You only have to add a tail
And it turns into j.

g and j and p and q
Their tails are really great.
Two curl back and one curls front
And one just hangs there straight.

The Write Rhymes *(cont.)*

These rhymes teach slanted lines and the new "feather" stroke. They also introduce the letters **v**, **w**, **x**, **y**, **z**, **f**, **t**, and **s**. For an enlarged version of the rhymes below, see pages 143, 185, 189, and 198.

w, v, and x, y, z —
All these letters are great ones;
Although we know they cross or slant
Their lines are always straight ones.

Two more letters that I know
Are long ones, l and k.
l stands very straight and tall
But k, it walks away.

f and t, I watch to see
That they cross on the line.
f is like a candy cane,
And t is straight and fine.

Now curve this way and curve that way
There is no need to guess.
It curls around just like a snake;
It is the letter s.

The Write Rhymes *(cont.)*

The last four rhymes use hook strokes, which are the same ones introduced as "tails" in Section 2 but with different placement. These rhymes also teach the letters **n**, **m**, **r**, and **u**. For an enlarged version of the rhymes below, see pages 223, 231, 236, and 241.

If you mix up n and m
I'll say you are to blame.
n has one hook, m has two
And so they're not the same.

h, it also has a hook
And looks quite like the others,
You make it with a big, long stem;
I guess that they are brothers.

So now begin to make an n
But please don't go too far.
You start to make the hook, then stop —
And that's the letter r!

Now we have one letter left,
And that's the letter u.
It sits up just like a cup
And now our song is through.

Write Rhymes Poster

When I write my ABC's,
I have an easy plan.
I sit up straight and sing my song
And do the best I can.

Some letters are quite short and fat,
And some of them are tall,
Some have stems and some have tails —
I try to make them all!

The Sing Write Along Scorecard

Reproduce the Scorecard (page 11) for each student. Use the Scorecard to document the progress of each student. The five sections of the book are represented on the Scorecard and the sections are divided to show each new stroke or letter as it is presented.

The first chart on the Scorecard shows the skills presented in this book. After the child has shown mastery of a skill, find the corresponding square on the chart and mark it in some way, such as by coloring it or gluing on a star.

The second chart on the Scorecard shows the lowercase letters of the alphabet in sequence. After the child has shown mastery of a letter, find the corresponding square on the chart and mark it in some way, such as by coloring it or gluing on a star. Marking each of the letters when mastery is acquired will help reinforce the alphabet, as well as allow the child to see his or her progress. This chart can also be used as a quick reference tool to determine which letters still need to be learned.

The Assessment Pages in each Review section of the book will provide the necessary information for completing the Scorecard.

The Scorecard, along with the Certificate of Completion (page 288), should be used to document mastery. The two forms may be placed in a student's portfolio and/or shared with parents.

Scorecard

Scorecard for ______________________

Skill Mastery							
Section	Skills						Notes
1. Before We Sing	o	l	•	-			
Sing Write Along	o	a	c	e	b	d	
2. Before We Sing	l	ı	J	ɭ			
Sing Write Along	l	i	j	g	q	p	
3. Before We Sing	/	\					
Sing Write Along	v	w	y	x	z		
4. Before We Sing	ɾ						
Sing Write Along	k	f	t	s			
5. Before We Sing	ɿ	ɭ					
Sing Write Along	n	m	h	r	u		

Alphabet Mastery												
a	b	c	d	e	f	g	h	i	j	k	l	m
n	o	p	q	r	s	t	u	v	w	x	y	z

Section 1

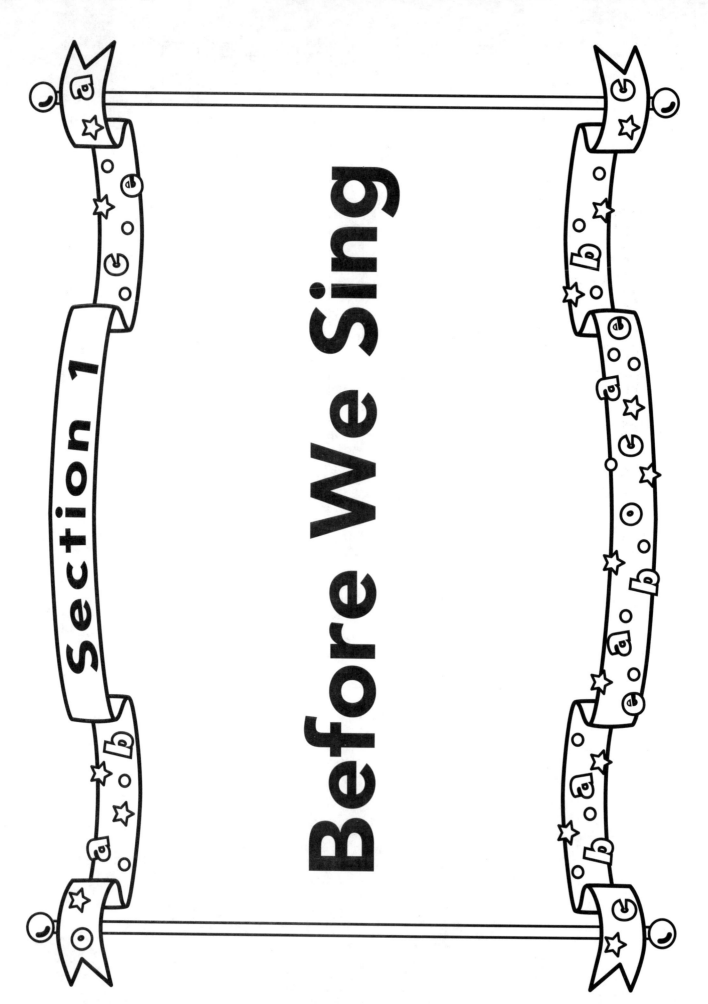

Before We Sing

Circles, Lines, Dots, and Spacing

This is a circle.

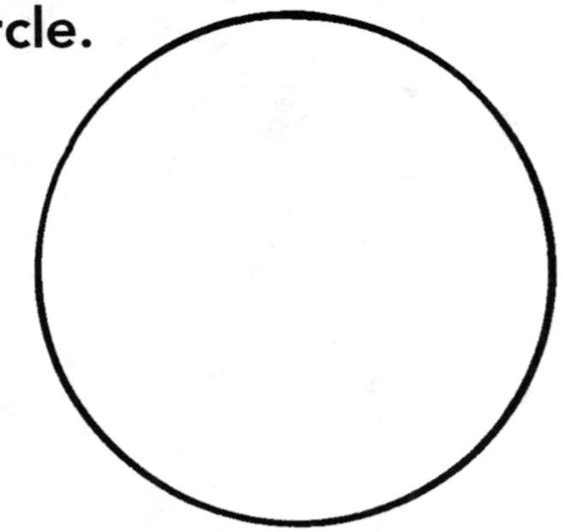

A circle is round. It is as around as —

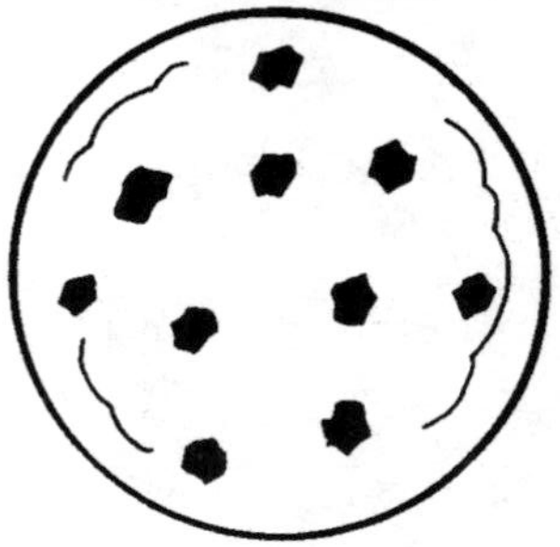

a cookie

a balloon

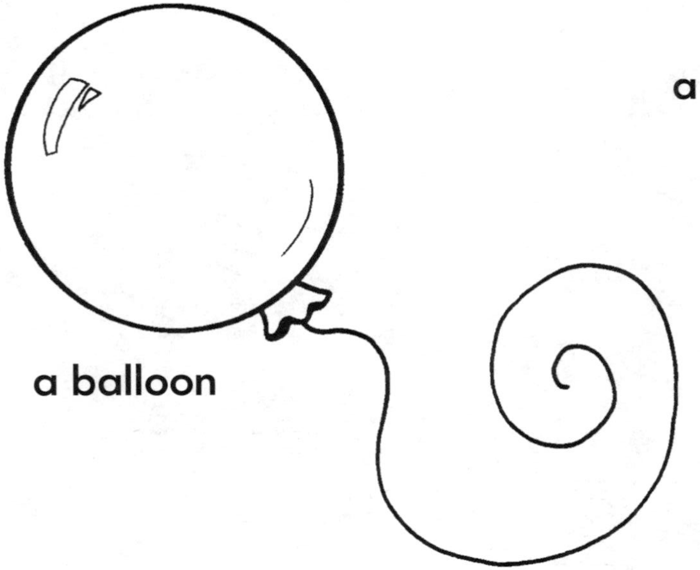

a wheel

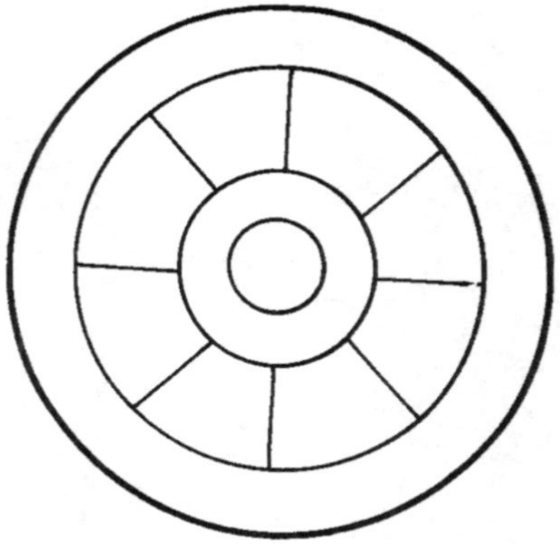

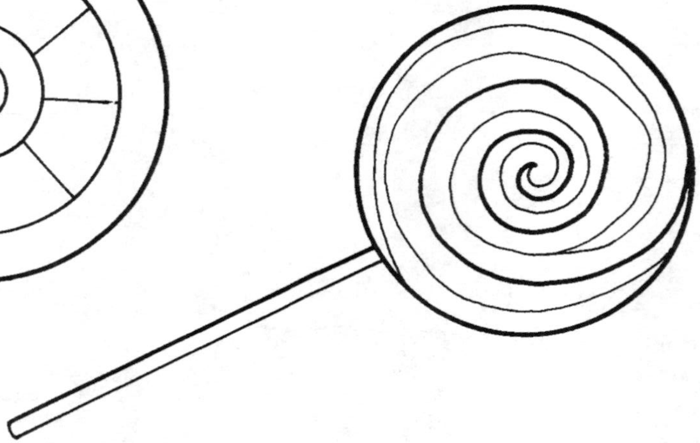

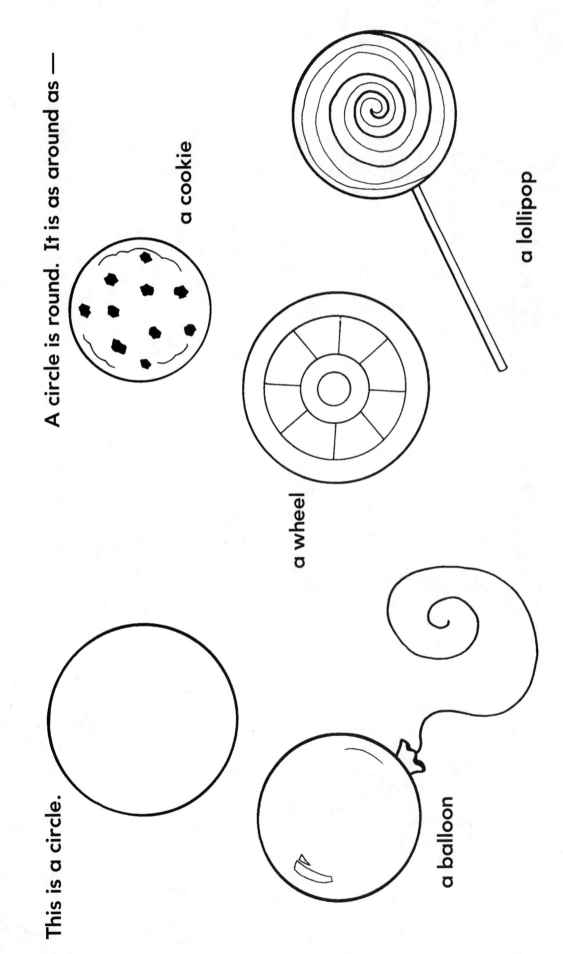

a lollipop

Circles, Lines, Dots and Spacing *(cont.)*

Can you trace some circles?

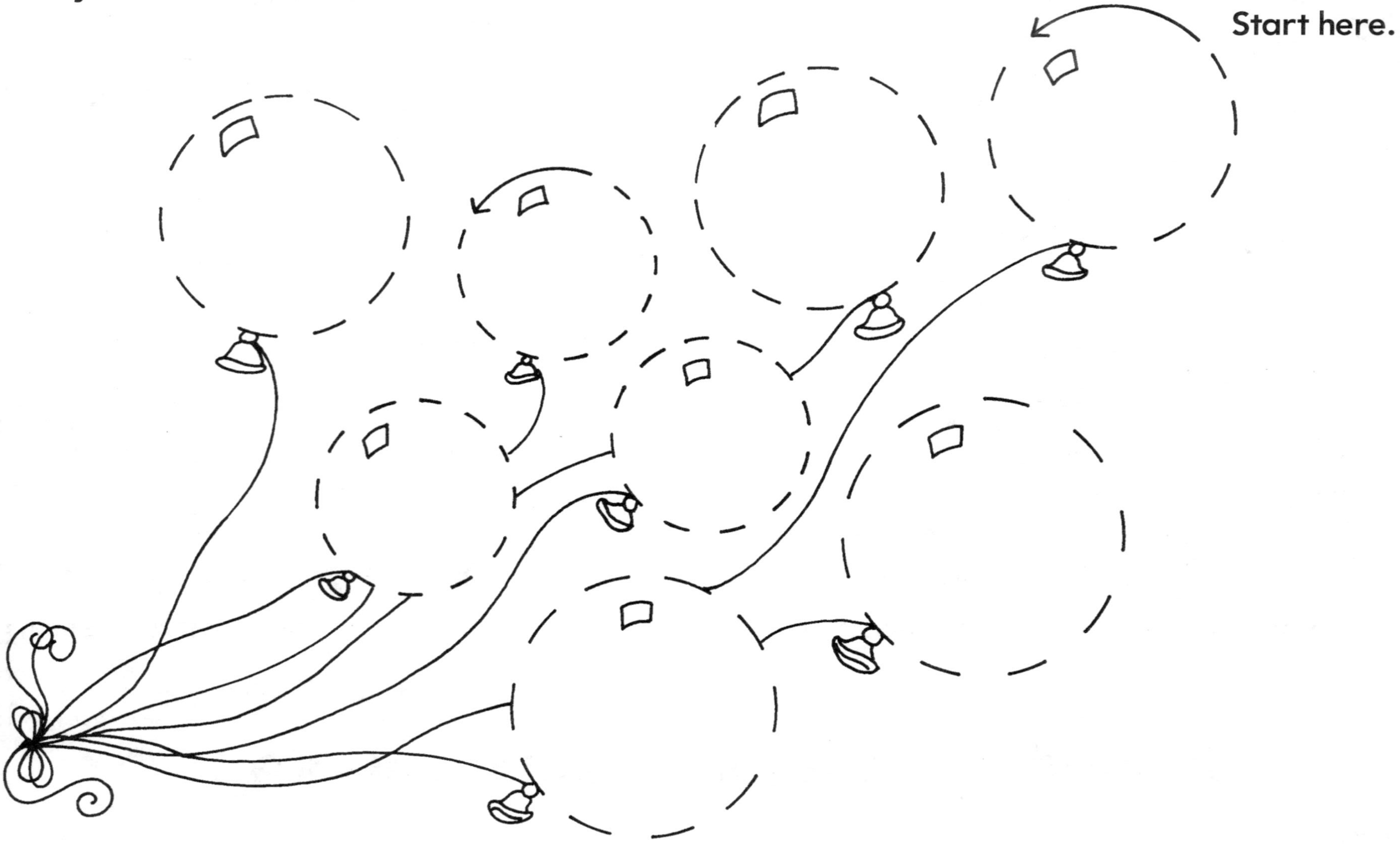

Circles, Lines, Dots and Spacing *(cont.)*

Here are some more circles for you to trace.

bells

oranges

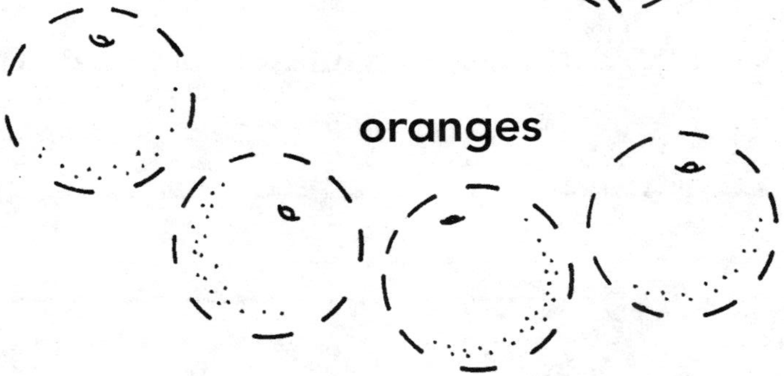

flowers

grapes

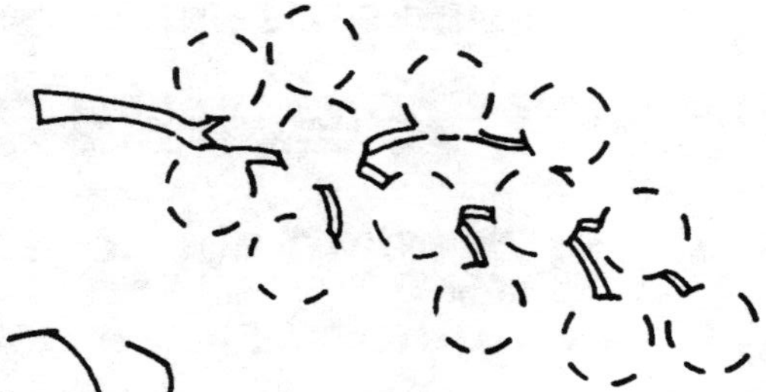

a big ball

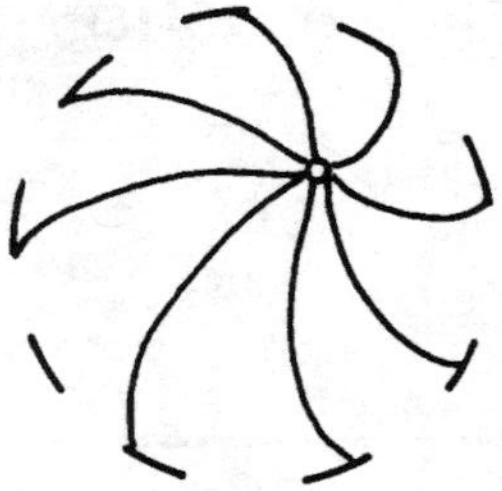

buttons

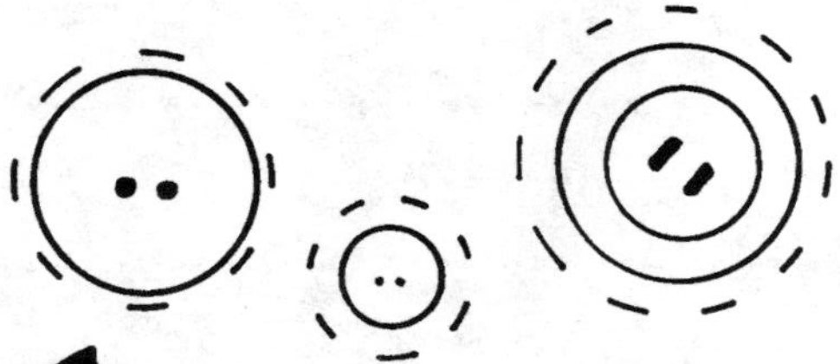

a snowman

Circles, Lines, Dots, and Spacing *(cont.)*

It is easy to make big and little circles when you have some lines to help you make them neatly. We use guide lines to help us.

Guide lines look like this:

The bottom line is very dark. Your circles can sit on this line.

The top line is very light. The very top of your big circles will touch this line, but they will never go any higher. It is the tallest a big circle can be when you write it on the guide lines.

The middle line, which is dotted, is in between the other two lines. It is halfway between the dark bottom guide line and the light top guide line. The very top of your small circles will touch the dotted middle guide line, but they will never go any higher. The dotted middle line is the tallest a small circle can be when you write it on the guide lines.

Circles, Lines, Dots, and Spacing *(cont.)*

Can you find the bottom guide line? Can you find the middle guide line? Can you find the top guide line?

Let's look at some big circles that are sitting on guide lines. See how neat they can be?

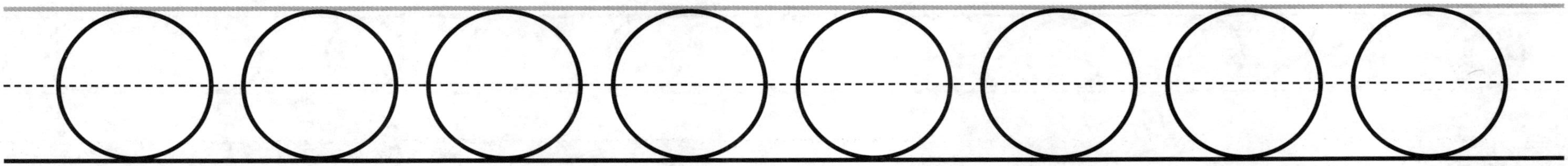

The circles sit on the dark bottom guide line. The tops of the circles touch the light top line. Can you trace these big circles on the guide lines?

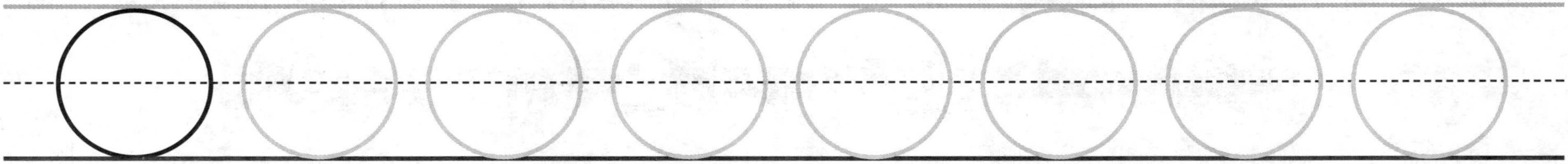

Circles, Lines, Dots, and Spacing *(cont.)*

You can make little circles on the guide lines, too. They sit on the dark bottom guide line, just like the big circles but they do not touch the light top guide line. The tops of little circles touch the dotted middle guide line.

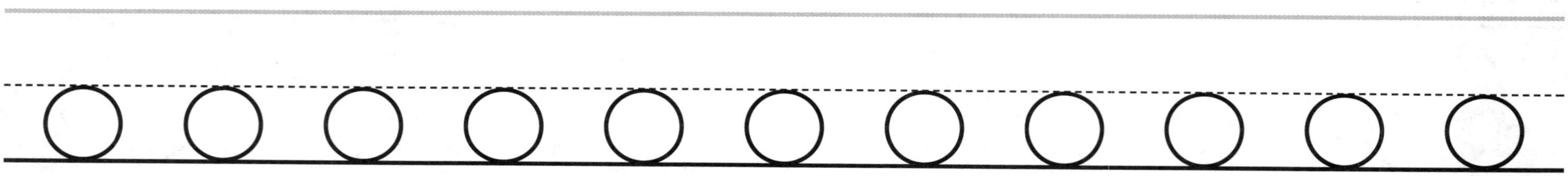

Trace these little circles. The guide lines will help you to keep them neat.

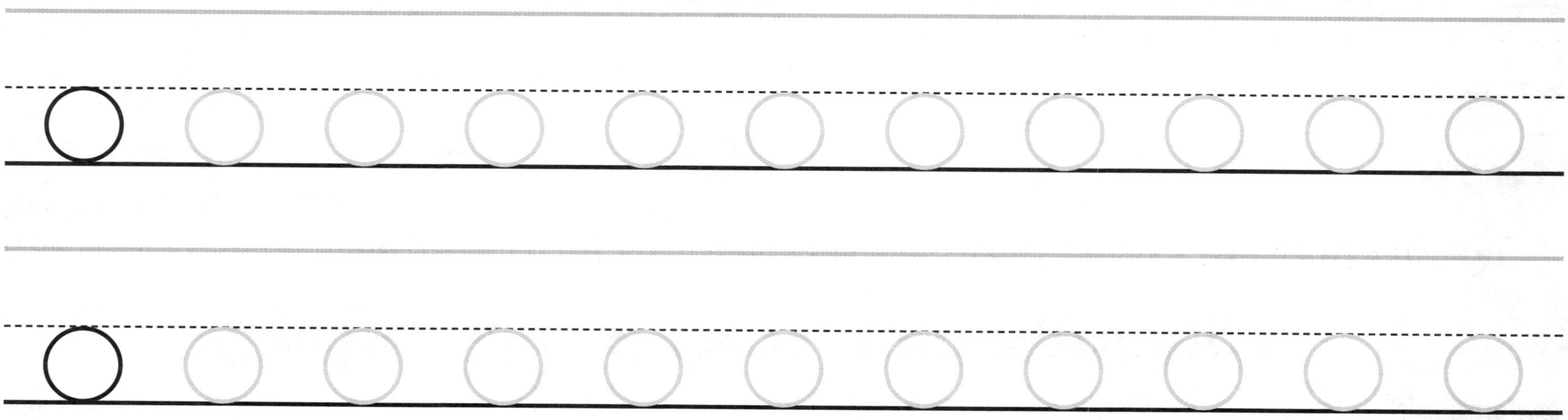

Circles, Lines, Dots, and Spacing *(cont.)*

Now let's mix up the big and little circles. Can you make both of them? Do they sit neatly on the bottom guide line?

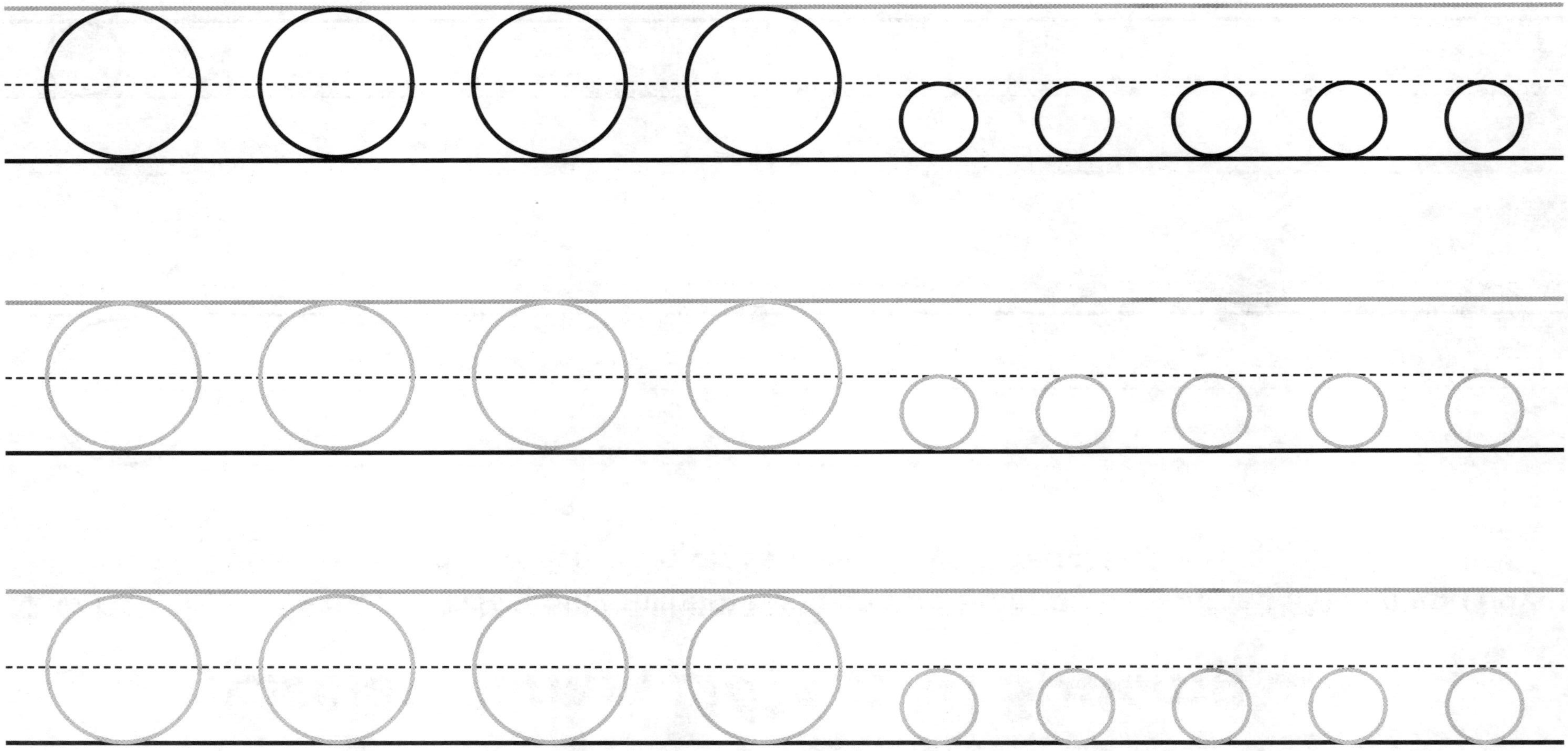

Circles, Lines, Dots, and Spacing *(cont.)*

Now let's try some more circles, only this time you can do them all by yourself! When you have finished, find your best and neatest circle and show it to your teacher.

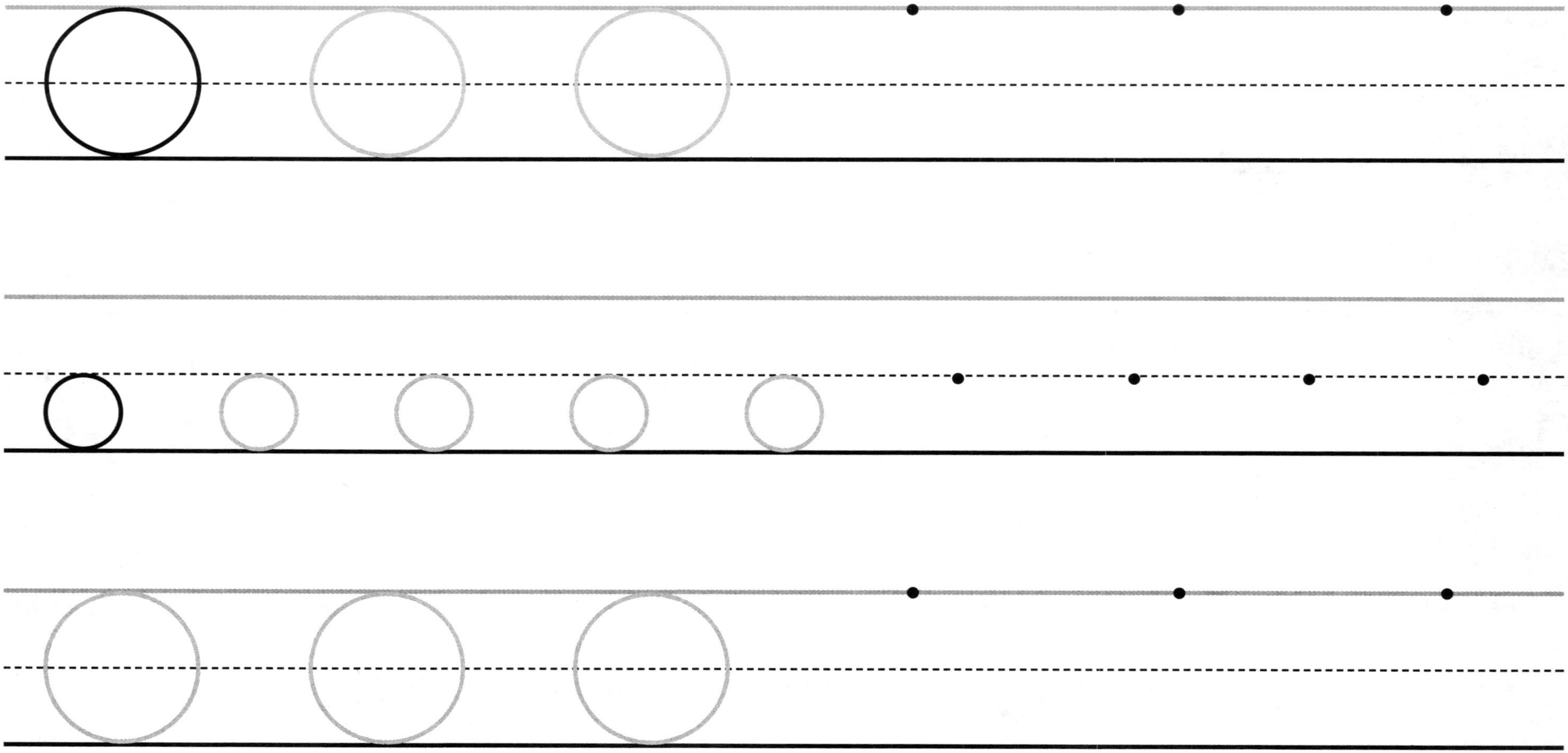

Circles, Lines, Dots, and Spacing *(cont.)*

These are straight lines.
They are big.

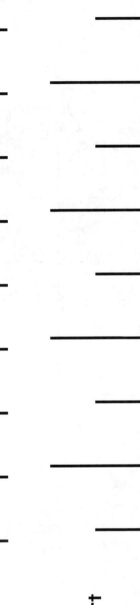

These are straight lines, too.
They are little.

To make a straight line, start
at the top and pull down.

Can you trace the straight lines to make sticks on these lollipops?

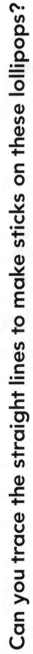

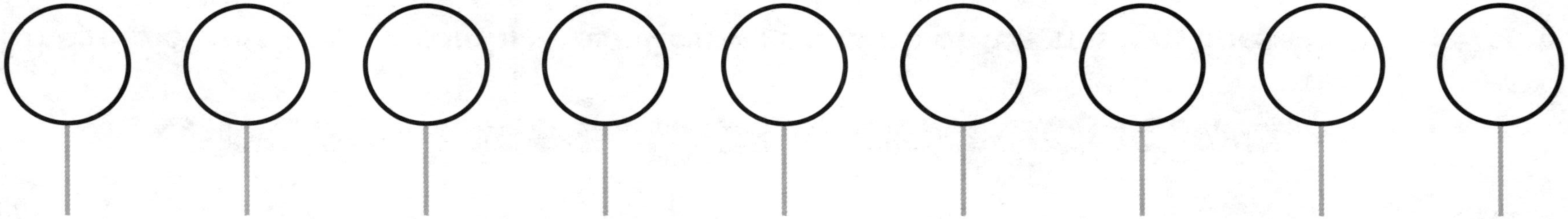

Circles, Lines, Dots, and Spacing *(cont.)*

All of these pictures have straight lines. Can you find all of the straight lines and trace them?

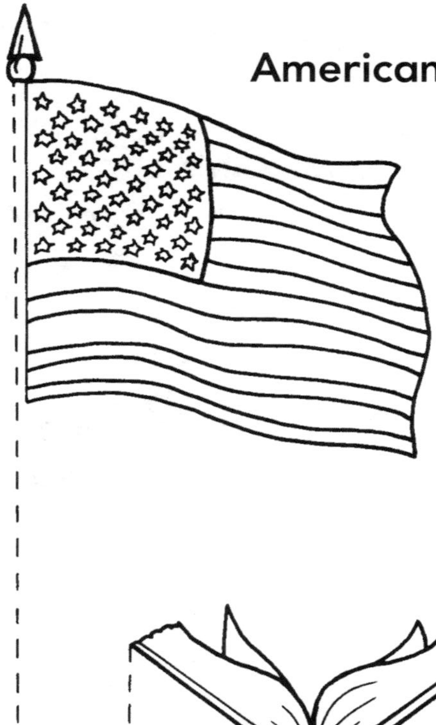

American flag

a picture frame

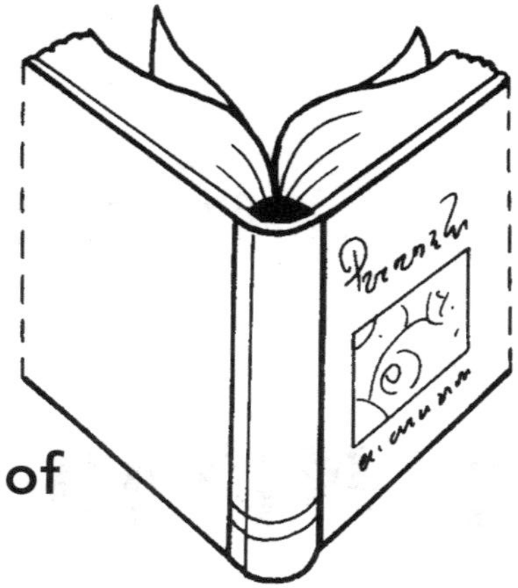

the sides of
a book

pens and pencils

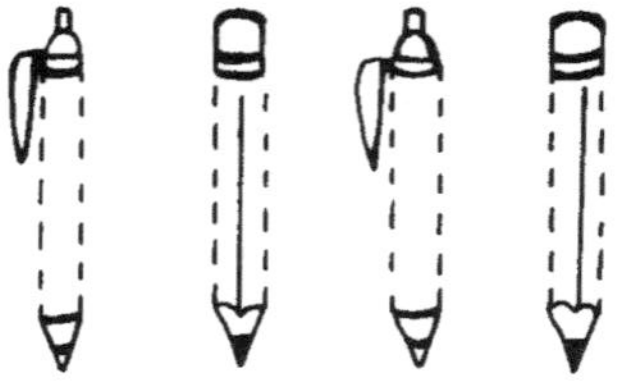

a big birthday present

Circles, Lines, Dots, and Spacing *(cont.)*

All of these have straight lines, too. Can you trace the straight lines?

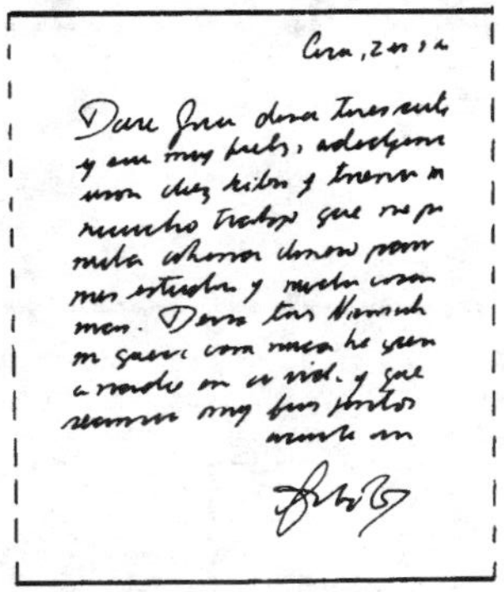

a letter

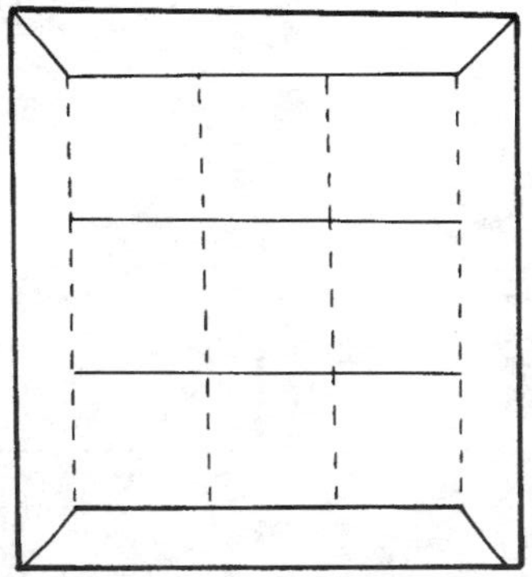

panes in a window

the legs of this chair

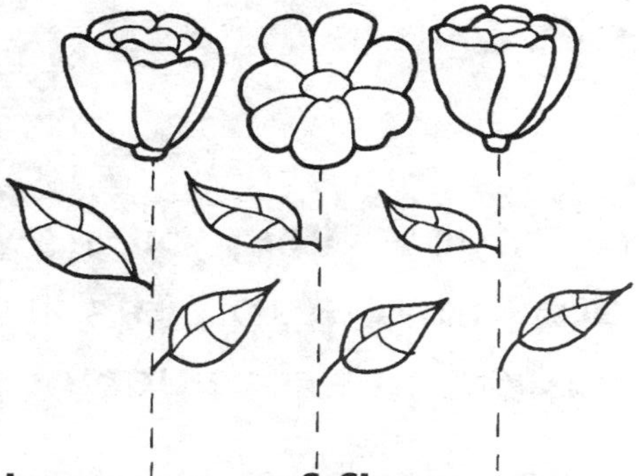

the stems of flowers

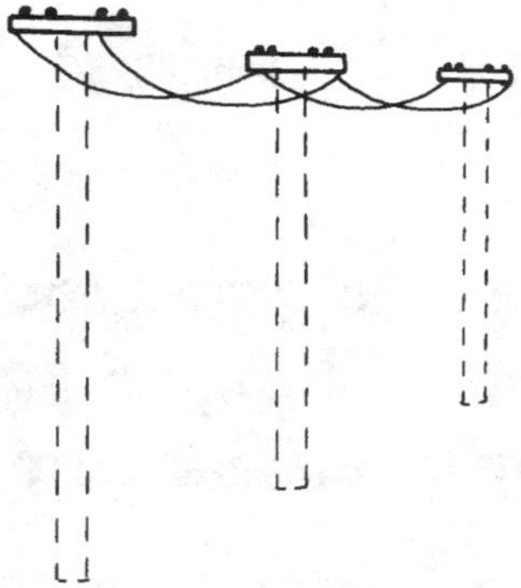

telephone poles

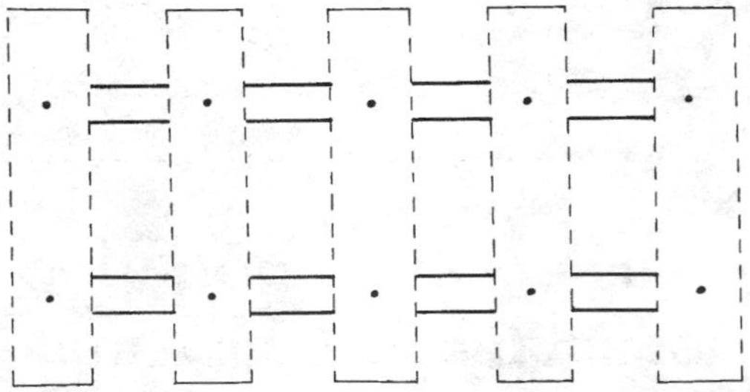

fences

Circles, Lines, Dots, and Spacing *(cont.)*

You can make nice, straight lines when you have the guide lines to help you. A big straight line will start at the light top guide line and will pull down all the way to the dark bottom guide line. A straight line stands very tall and does not wobble or bend.

These big straight lines are on the guide lines.

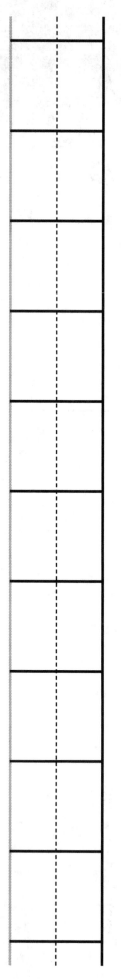

Now you can trace these big straight lines.

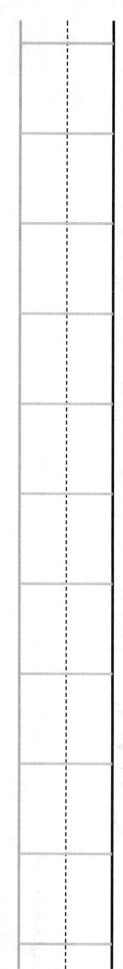

Circles, Lines, Dots, and Spacing *(cont.)*

Little straight lines are like the big straight lines in many ways. They stand up straight and do not wobble or bend. But they do not begin at the light top guide line. To make a small straight line, you will begin on the dotted middle guide line and pull down to the dark bottom guide line.

These little straight lines are on the guide lines.

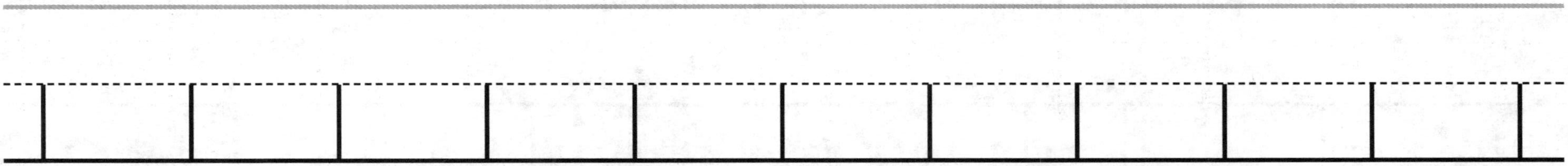

Try some here. Make sure each line sits on the dark bottom guide line.

Circles, Lines, Dots, and Spacing *(cont.)*

Now let's try some big straight lines together with some little straight lines. Remember to begin the big straight lines at the light top guide line and the little straight lines at the dotted middle guide line. Both big and little straight lines will sit on the dark bottom guide line.

Now try making some by yourself. How do they look? Are they straight and neat?

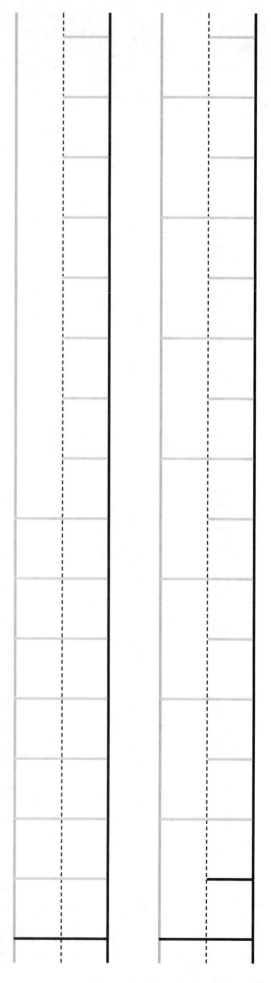

Circles, Lines, Dots, and Spacing *(cont.)*

Lines and circles together can make lollipops. Try making some here.

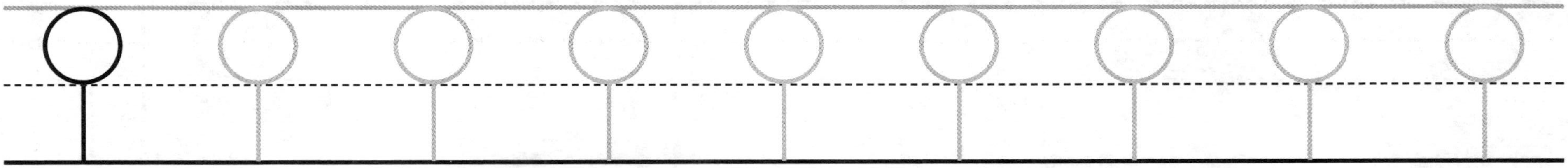

Now let's try putting some circles and lines on the guide lines. They are the same strokes that you used when you made lollipops.

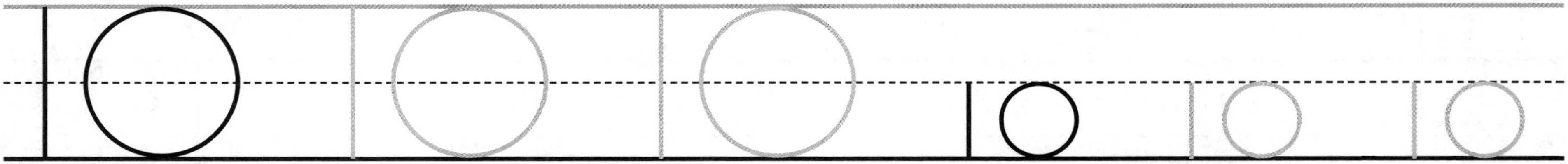

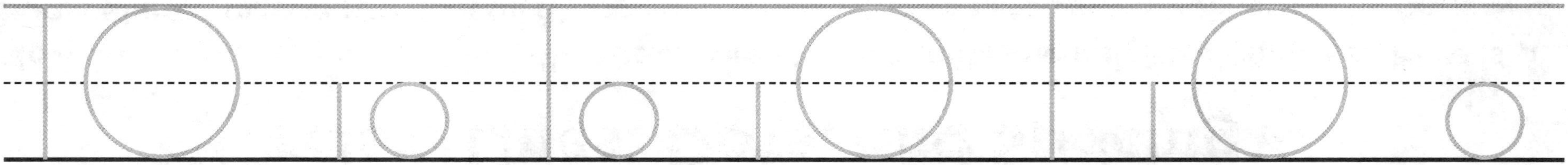

How do your straight lines and circles look? Are they nice and neat?

Circles, Lines, Dots, and Spacing *(cont.)*

Now you can make big circles, little circles, big straight lines, and little straight lines. Here is a page where you can practice all of them.

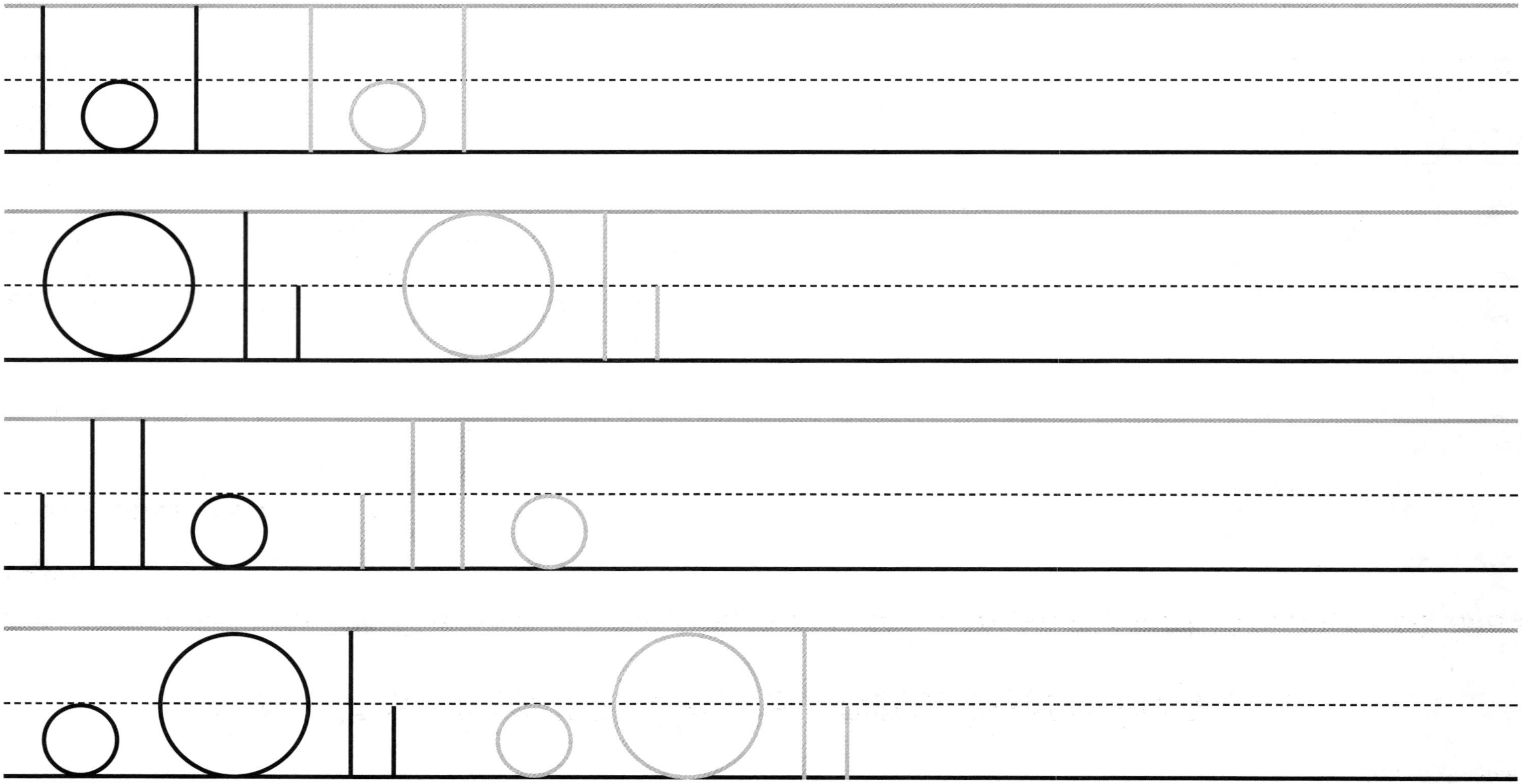

Circles, Lines, Dots, and Spacing *(cont.)*

A dot is a little, neat filled-in circle that you make with the tip of your pencil. A dot is small and round.

A dot looks like this.

It does NOT look like this.

Dots can be used to make eyes. Put some eyes in these faces.

Can you put a dot inside each lollipop? See if you can put a dot in the center, or middle, of each lollipop. The first one has been done for you.

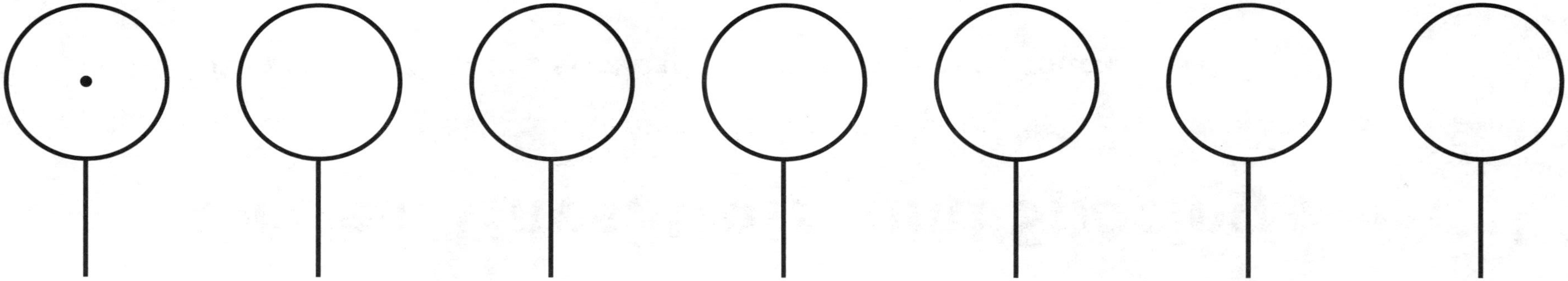

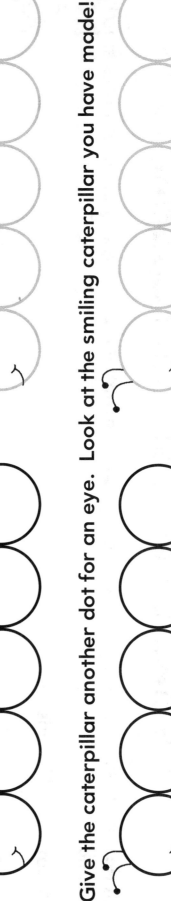

Circles, Lines, Dots, and Spacing *(cont.)*

Here are five little circles that are so close together that they touch.

Can you make some circles?

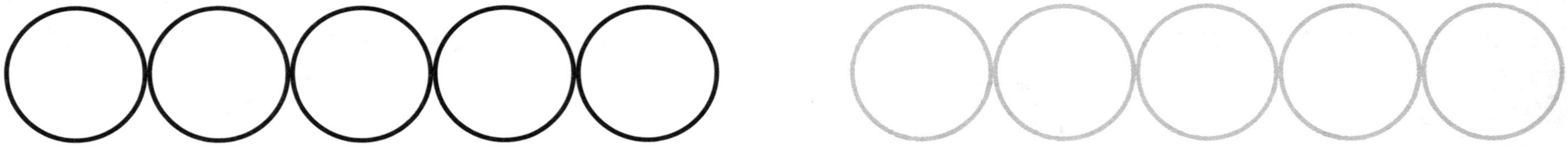

If you add two neat dots to the first circle, you can make a caterpillar!

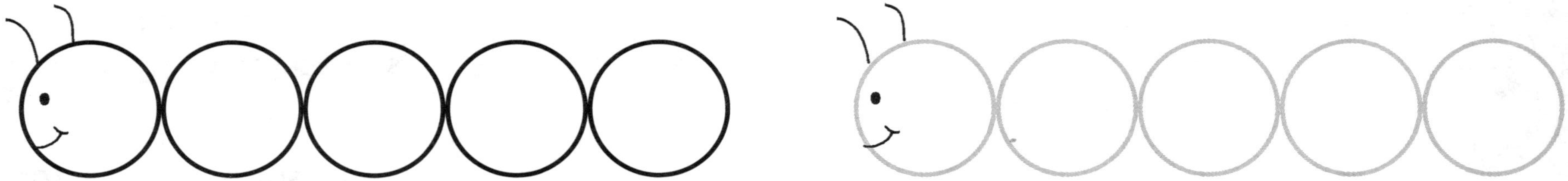

Give the caterpillar another dot for an eye. Look at the smiling caterpillar you have made!

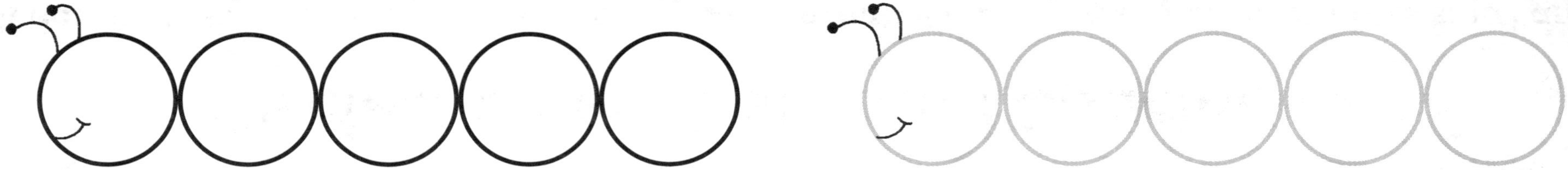

Circles, Lines, Dots, and Spacing *(cont.)*

Now let's put some of those caterpillars on guide lines and see how neat they can be. Remember to make your circles round and fat.

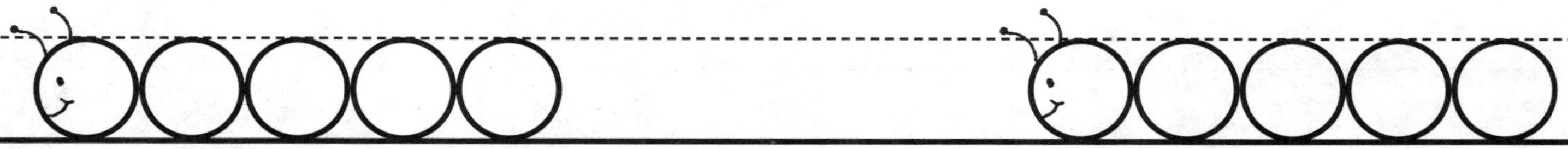

Here are some caterpillars for you to trace.

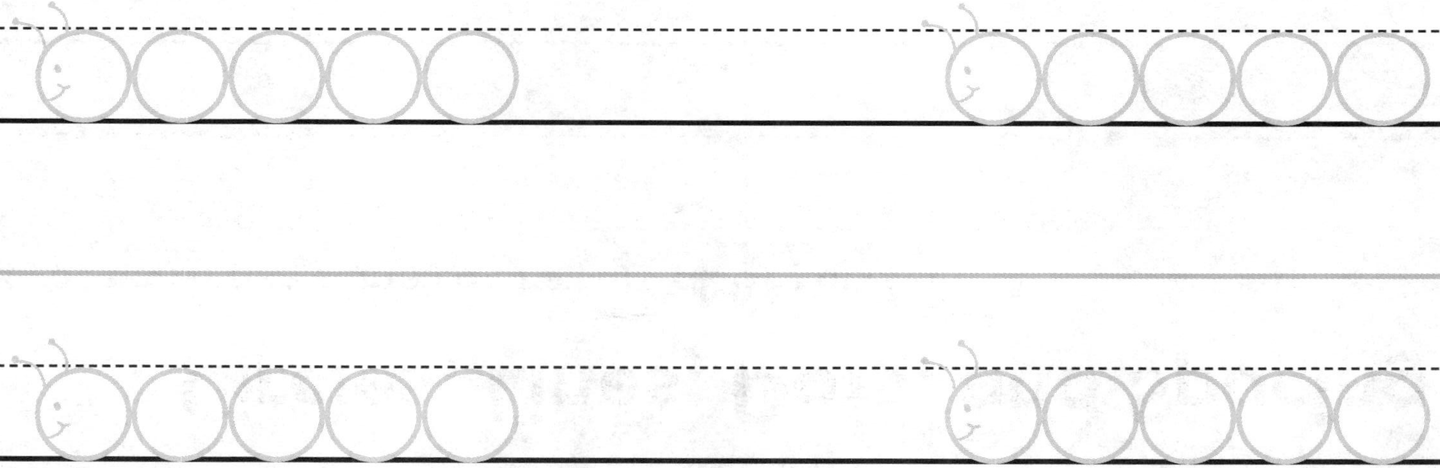

Circles, Lines, Dots, and Spacing *(cont.)*

Now you can make some caterpillars all by yourself.

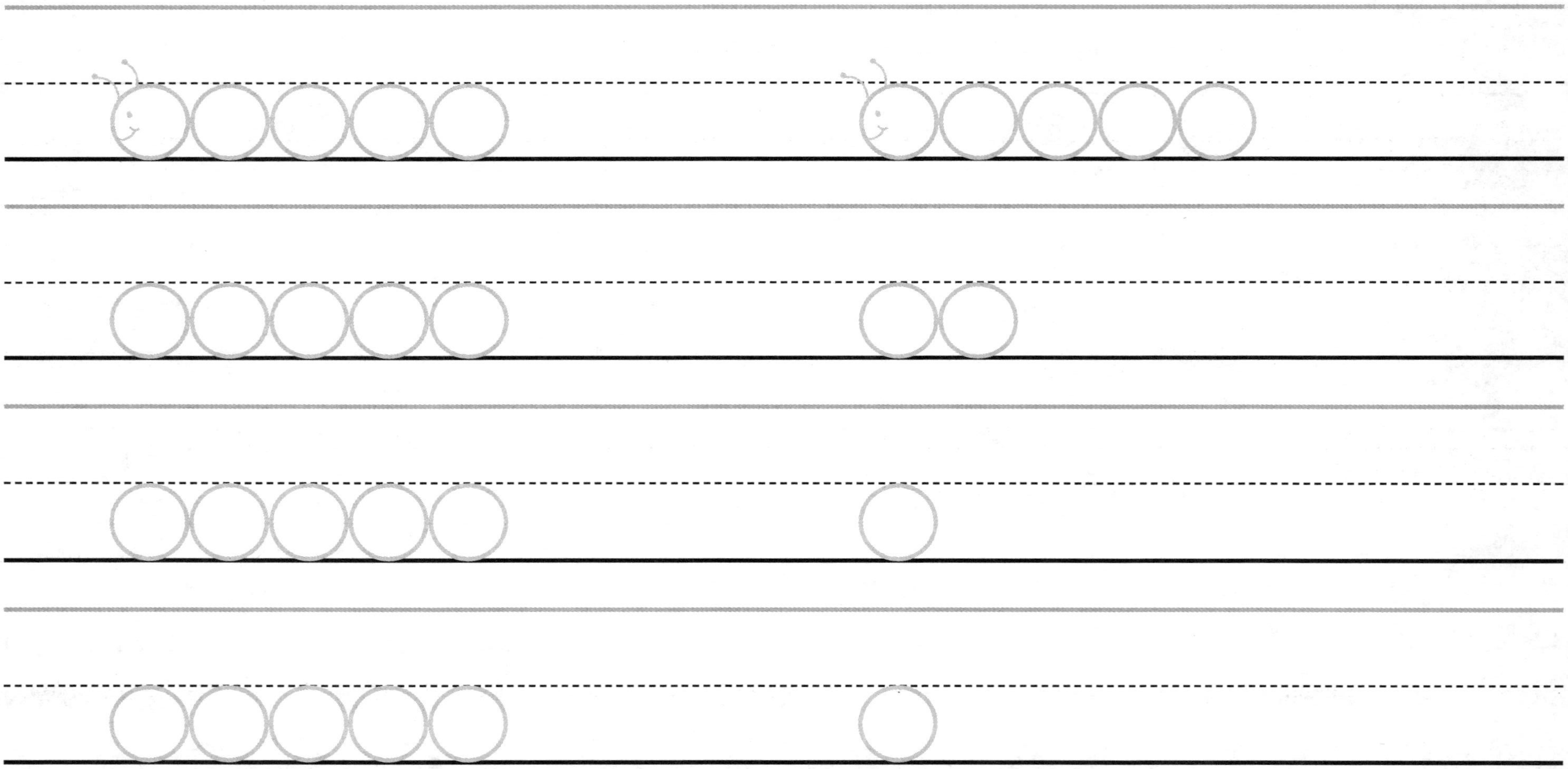

Find the caterpillar you think is your very best and color it green!

Circles, Lines, Dots, and Spacing *(cont.)*

There should be **spaces** between letters. Spaces are the places that are empty and do not have any marks or letters. Spaces make your work look neat, and they keep letters from crowding together.

Crowded letters look like this.

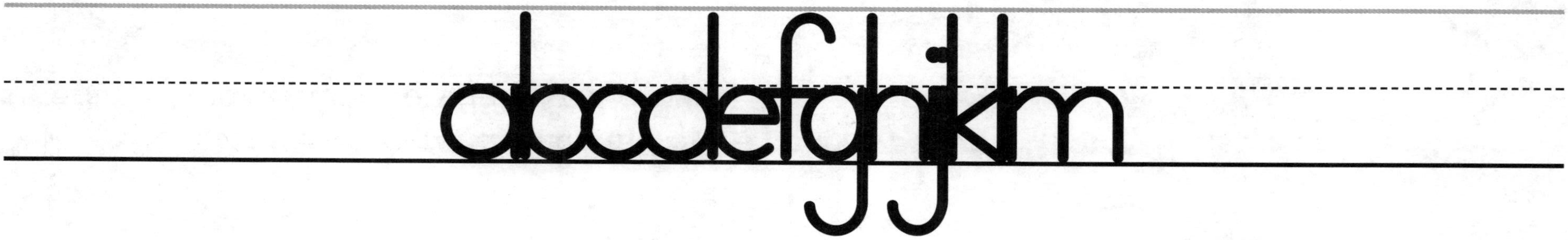

It is easier to see letters when there are spaces between them. Can you find the spaces between these letters?

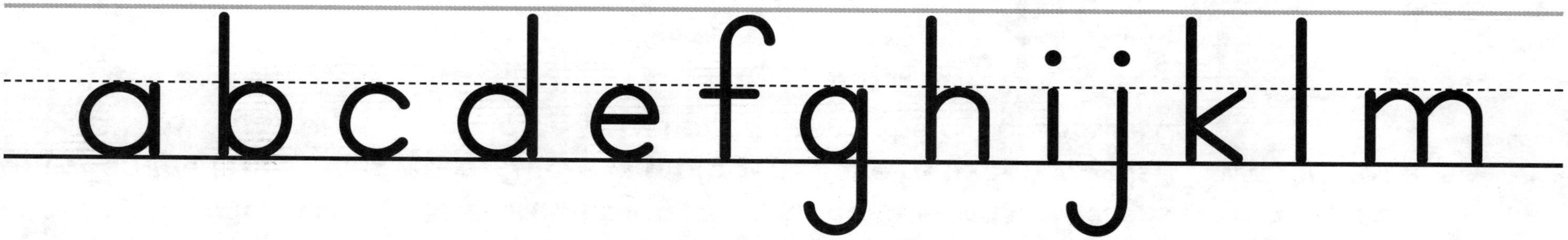

Our Guide Paper (page 287) uses spaces between each set of writing lines. Those spaces help make the letters you write look neat, and they keep the letters with "tails" from hanging down into the guide line underneath.

Circles, Lines, Dots, and Spacing *(cont.)*

Spaces help a lot when letters are put together to make words. There is a small space between the letters in a word. There is a bigger space between words. If we did not use spaces between words, it would be very hard to read the different words.

Canyoureadthis?

Words are a lot easier to read when there are spaces between them. The spaces keep the letters that make each word in a little group.

Can you read this?

Remember to put little spaces between the letters you write and bigger spaces between words. That way your letters and words will look neat and they will be easy for you to read.

Section 1

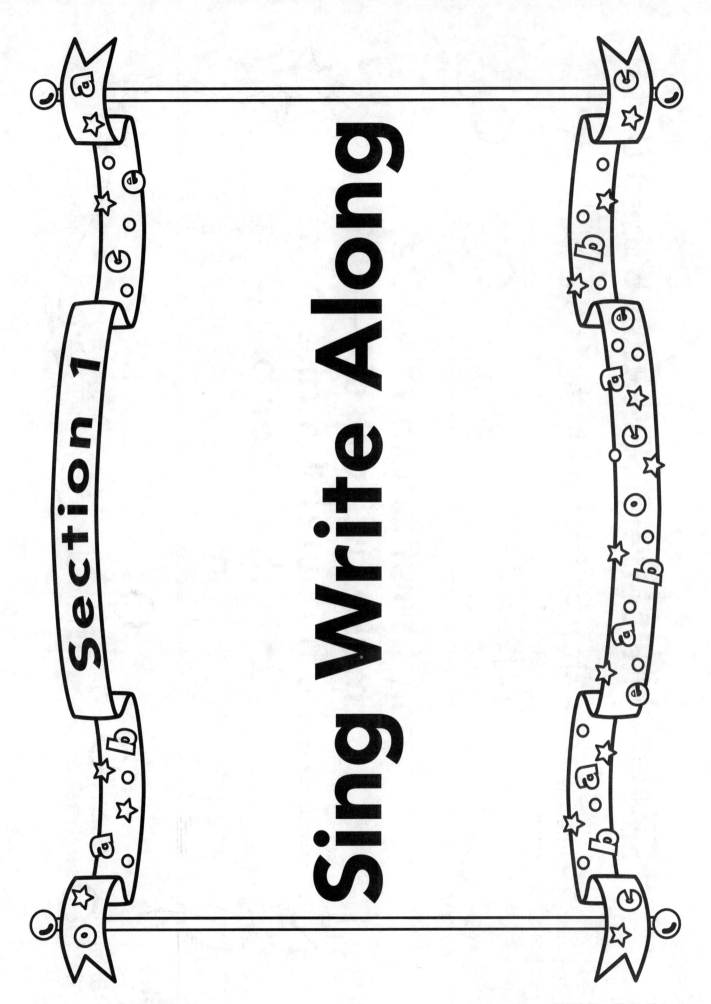

Sing Write Along

Teaching the Letters o, a, c, e, b, and d

Write Rhymes Poster for the Letter o

When I first begin to write,
I make a circle, so —
I make it round; I make it fat.
It is the letter o.

Teaching the Letters o, a, c, e, b, and d

Do you remember that caterpillar?

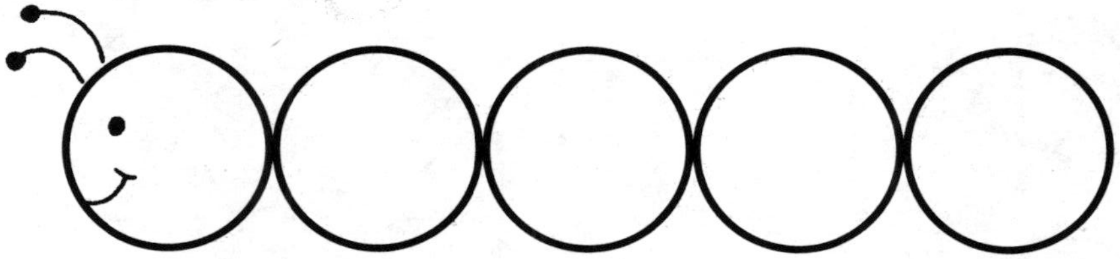

It is made of round, fat circles. Each time you made one of those round, fat circles, you were making a letter!

You made the letter o!

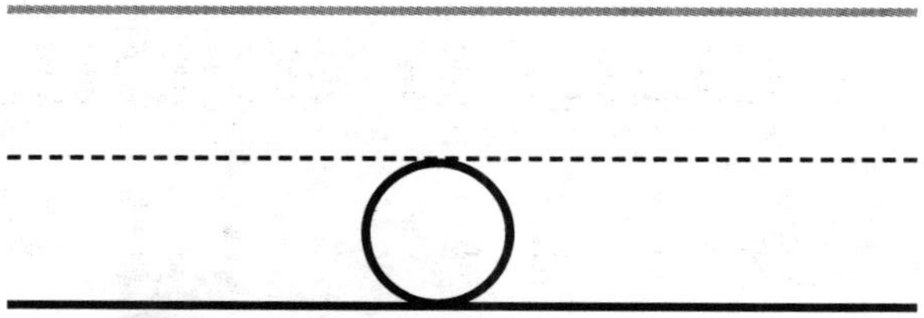

The little letter **o** reaches from the dotted middle guide line to the dark bottom guide line. Now you can make the letter **o** by tracing the letters. Leave a space between the letters, so they do not touch each other.

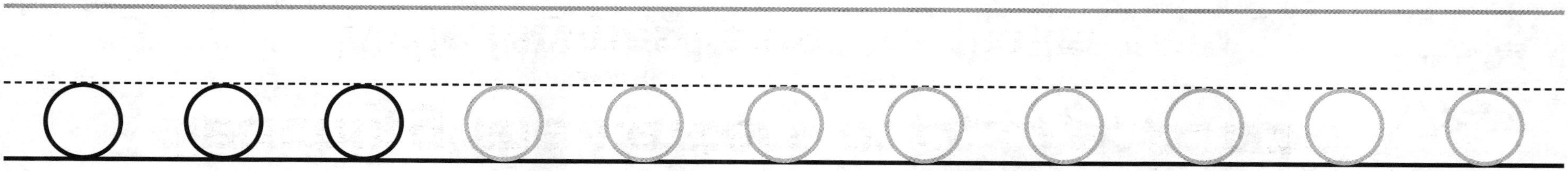

Teaching the Letters o, a, c, e, b, and d *(cont.)*

The round, fat circles that we have made are the same as the letter **o**. Here are some shapes that use the letter **o**.

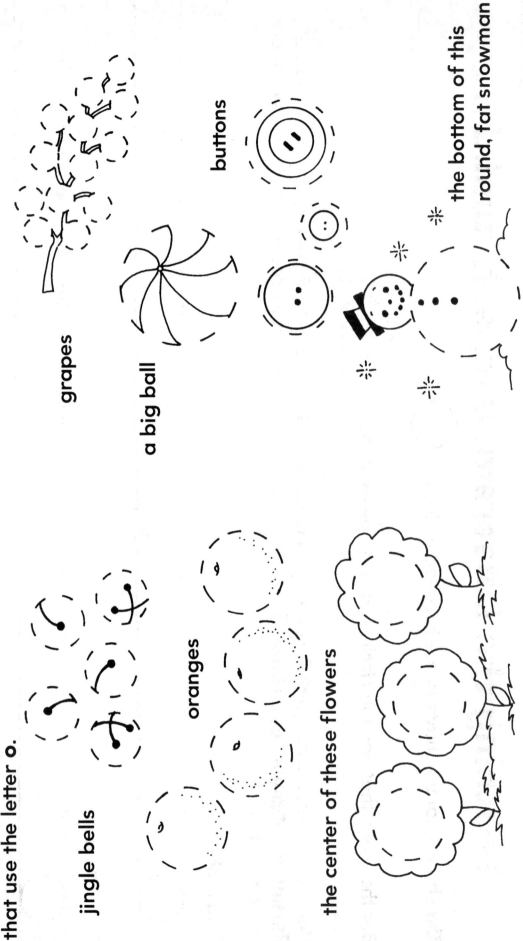

jingle bells

oranges

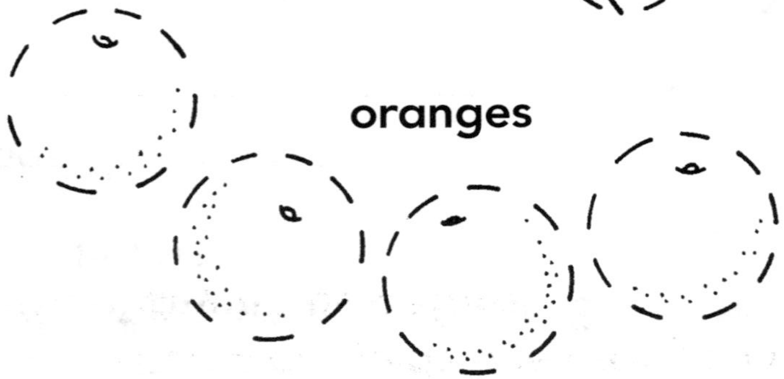

the center of these flowers

grapes

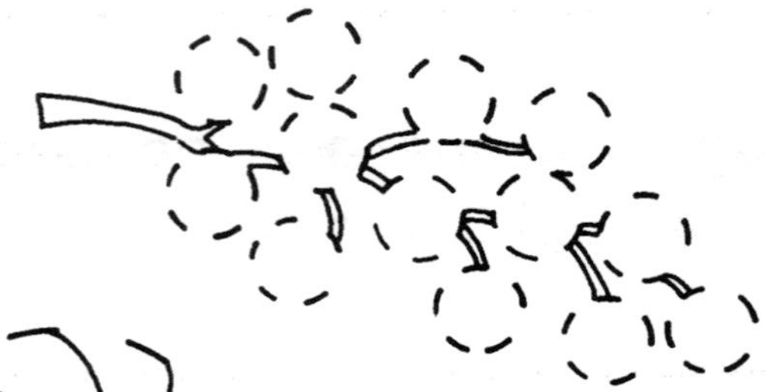

a big ball

buttons

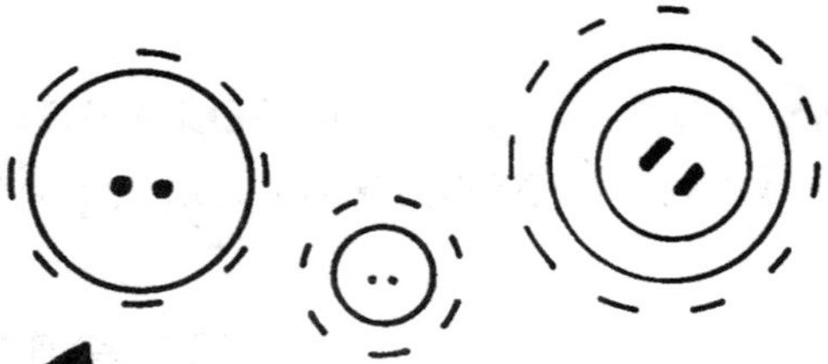

the bottom of this round, fat snowman

Teaching the Letters o, a, c, e, b, and d *(cont.)*

The shape that you have made is called a **circle**. 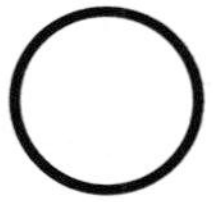

But the letter that has the circle shape is called an **o**. 

Here is the letter **o** on guide lines for you to write. It is so easy to do because you have made the letter **o** many times before!

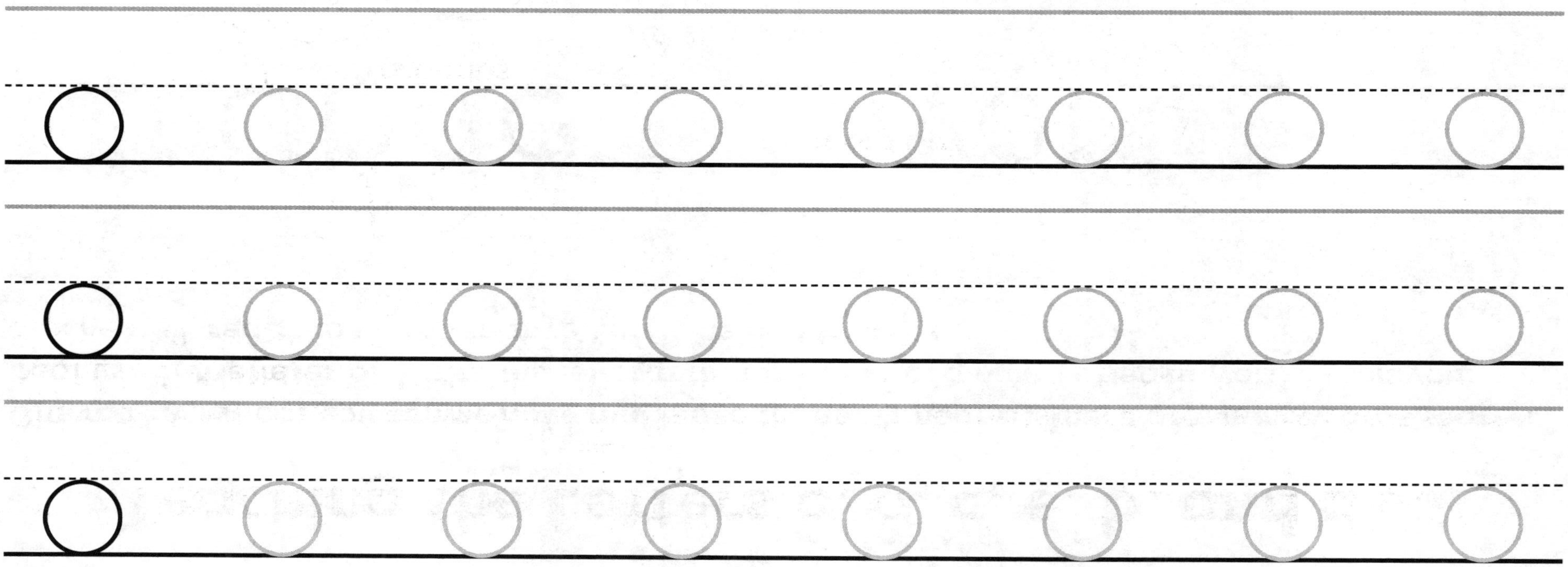

Teaching the Letters o, a, c, e, b, and d *(cont.)*

Did you know that you can now write a letter of the alphabet? There are many words that begin with the letter o. Write the letter o that is at the beginning of each word. Then your teacher will read the words that you have helped to write!

orange over

old octopus

out open

Teaching the Letters o, a, c, e, b, and d *(cont.)*

Now practice writing your first alphabet letter (o) without any help!

o o

o o

o o

o o

Teaching the Letters o, a, c, e, b, and d *(cont.)*

Write Rhymes Poster for the Letters o, a, c, and e

o a c

o and a and c and e,
I know I won't mistake them.
They don't stick up; they don't
hang down
But sit right where I make them.

e o a

Teaching the Letters o, a, c, e, b, and d *(cont.)*

You can already make the letter **o**. You can already make a short straight line, too. That means that you can make another letter of the alphabet! If you make a circle first, then add a short, straight line that touches the right edge of the circle, you will have a new letter. The new letter is **a**!

a

a a a a a a a a a a

To make the letter **a**, just put together two strokes that you already know.

Teaching the Letters o, a, c, e, b, and d *(cont.)*

Practice writing the letter a. Make the circle part of the letter first. Then add the short straight line. Make sure the line touches the right edge of the circle. Say the name of the letter as you write it.

a a a a a a a a a a

a a a a a a a a a a

a a a a a a a a a a

Teaching the Letters o, a, c, e, b, and d *(cont.)*

Now you can make the letter a all by yourself! Say the name of the letter as you write it.

a a

a a

a a

a a

Teaching the Letters o, a, c, e, b, and d *(cont.)*

You can write two letters of the alphabet (**a** and **o**). Below are some words that begin with the letter **a** or the letter **o**. Ask your teacher to read the words to you. Then you can write an **a** or **o** to complete each word!

apple other

after alive

out ape

Teaching the Letters o, a, c, e, b, and d *(cont.)*

Here is the letter **o**.

o

The fish has made a new letter by taking a bite out of the letter **o**! The fish has made the letter **c**!

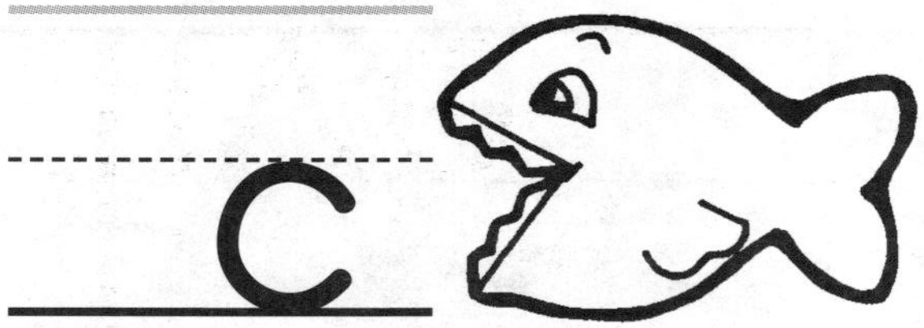

You can make the letter **c**. It is a circle that is not quite finished. You will begin to make a circle and then stop before you are done.

To write the letter **c**, begin your circle under the dotted middle guide line. Go up to touch the dotted middle guide line, circle around to the dark bottom guide line, and then begin to go up to finish the circle. But do not close the circle! Stop when you are part way up! Now try writing the letter **c**!

c c c c c c c c c c

Teaching the Letters o, a, c, e, b, and d *(cont.)*

Write the letter **c**. The arrow shows you which way to go. Remember to begin your circle under the dotted middle guide line, not on it. Make the circle part round and fat, just the way you have practiced.

c c

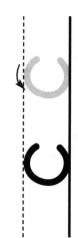

Practice writing the letter **c**. Say the name of the letter as you write it.

c c c c c c c c c c

c c c c c c c c c c

Teaching the Letters o, a, c, e, b, and d *(cont.)*

Now you can practice writing the letter c by yourself. Say the name of the letter as you write it.

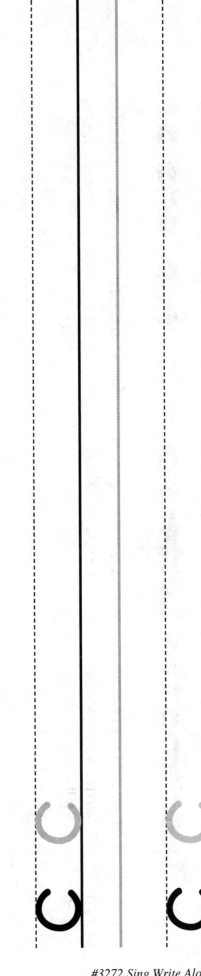

c c

c c

c c

c c

Teaching the Letters o, a, c, e, b, and d *(cont.)*

Here are some words that have the letters **o**, **a**, and **c**. Can you find and write all of them? Some are inside the word, so look carefully! When you are done, have your teacher say the words for you.

boat care

corn back

oak trace

Teaching the Letters o, a, c, e, b, and d *(cont.)*

The next letter is the letter **e**. It looks very much like the letter **c**, but it has an added part. The new part is a little line that goes from the rounded part of the **c** across to the beginning the **c**. Begin with the little line and then make the letter **c** the way you have learned. The arrows show you which way to go. You have made the letter e!

e

Practice writing the letter **e**. Say the name of the letter as you write it.

e e e e e e e e e e e

e e e e e e e e e e e

Teaching the Letters o, a, c, e, b, and d *(cont.)*

Write the letter **e**. Remember to make the little line first, and then make the letter **c**. Say the name of the letter as you write it.

e e e e e e e e e e e

e e e e e e e e e e e

e e e e e e e e e e e

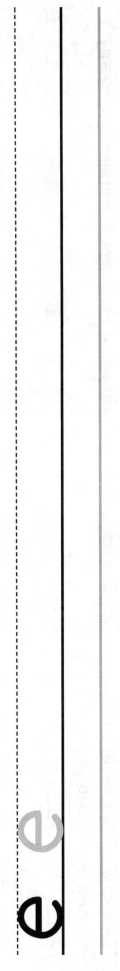

Teaching the Letters o, a, c, e, b, and d *(cont.)*

Now you can write the letter **e** all by yourself! Say the name of the letter as you write it.

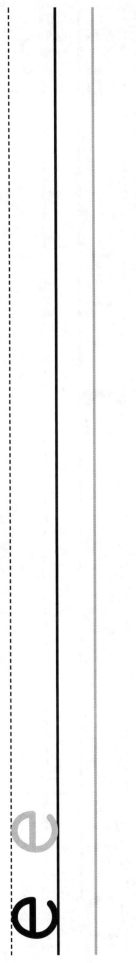

e e

e e

e e

e e

Teaching the Letters o, a, c, e, b, and d *(cont.)*

Here are all the letters you know (**o**, **c**, **a**, and **e**). Can you write each one? Remember to say the name of each letter as you write it.

o o o o o a a a a a

c c c c c e e e e e

a a a a a c c c c c

e e e e e o o o o o

Teaching the Letters o, a, c, e, b, and d *(cont.)*

All the letters you know (**o**, **a**, **c**, and **e**) are in these words. You will have to have sharp eyes to find all of them. Be sure to look at the beginning and end, as well as inside the words! Can you write all of them?

coat are

have look

snack same

Teaching the Letters o, a, c, e, b, and d *(cont.)*

Write Rhymes Poster for the Letters **a** and **d**

a d a

a and d are quite alike,
But I don't write the wrong one.
The stem on a is very short
And on the d a long one.

d d a

Teaching the Letters o, a, c, e, b, and d *(cont.)*

Look at the new letter that is next to the letter **a.** The new letter is the letter **d.** Can you see how **a** and **d** are different? The letter **a** has a short line, or stem. The line, or stem, that attaches to the letter **d** is a long one.

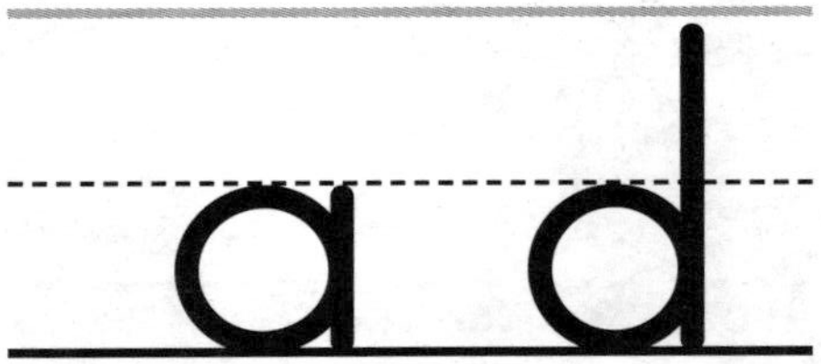

Both **a** and **d** begin with a fat, round circle. Then the stem will touch the right side of the circle. The letter **a** has a short line for a stem. But the letter **d** has a long line for a stem.

Practice writing the letter **d.** Say the name of the letter as you write it.

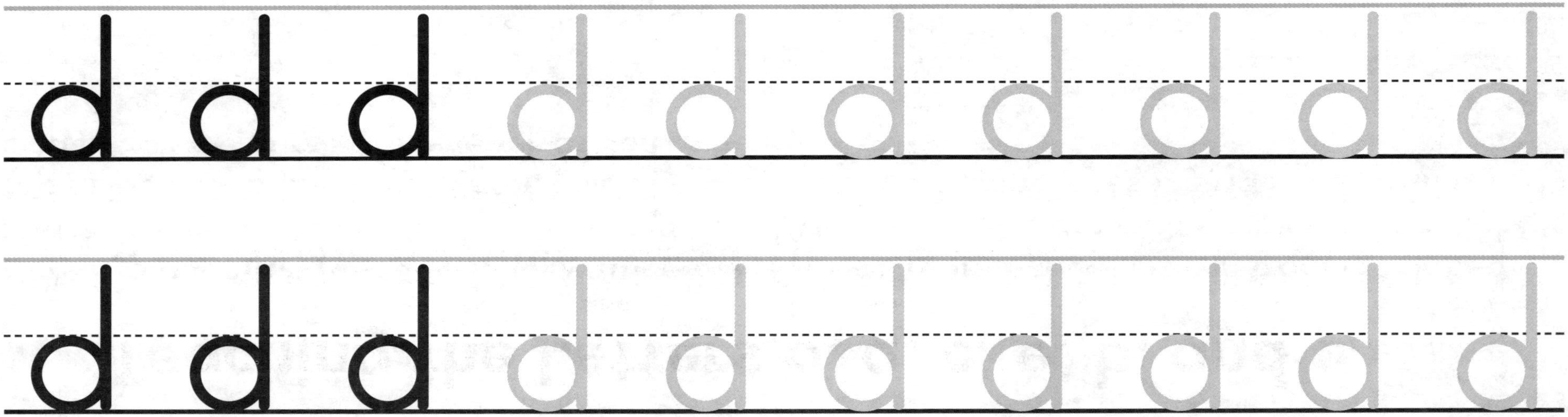

Teaching the Letters o, a, c, e, b, and d *(cont.)*

Here is a page for you to practice writing the letter **d**. Your circle will reach from the dotted middle guide line to the dark bottom guide line. The stem will reach all the way from the light top guide line to the dark bottom guide line. Be sure the stem touches the right side of the circle. Say the name of the letter as you write it.

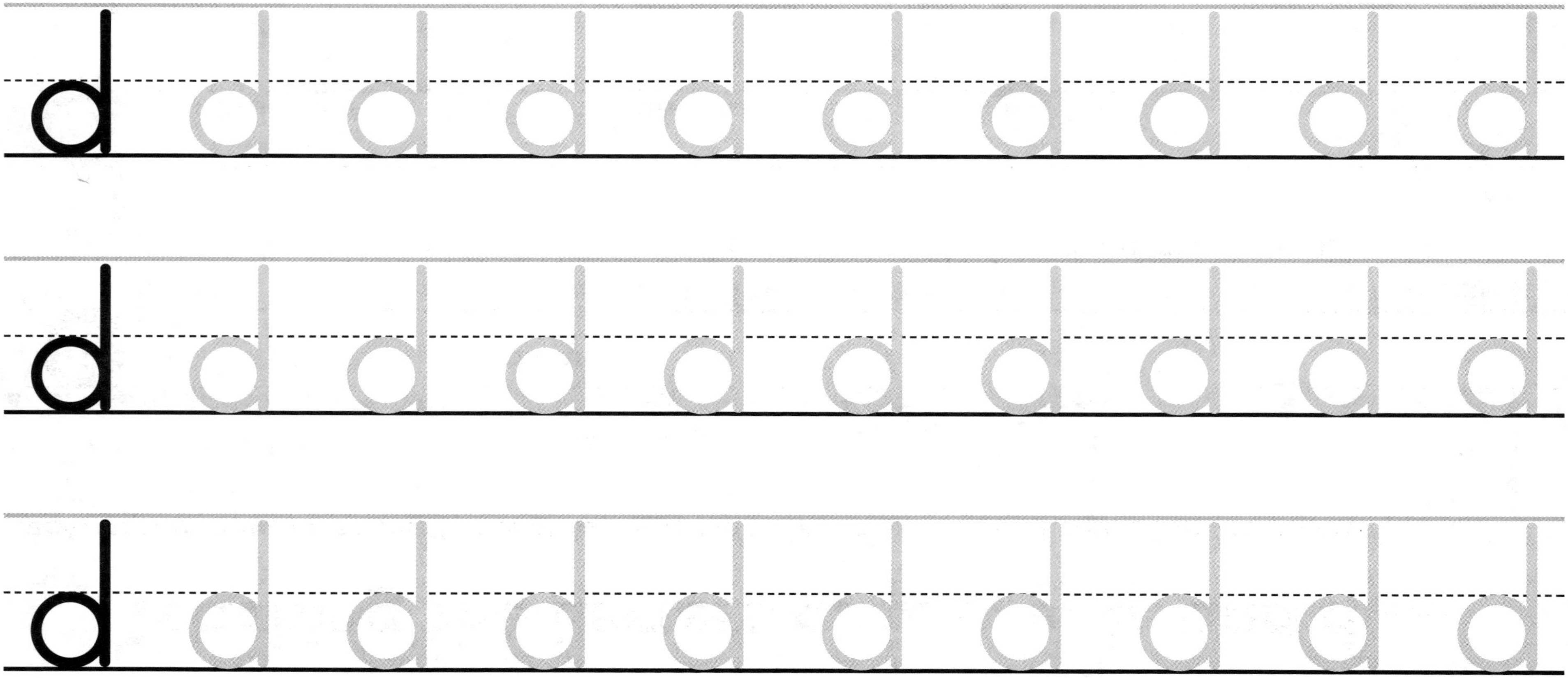

Teaching the Letters o, a, c, e, b, and d *(cont.)*

Now you can make the letter **d** all by yourself. Say the name of the letter as you write it.

d d

d d

d d

d d

Teaching the Letters o, a, c, e, b, and d *(cont.)*

Now let's practice writing the letters **a** and **d** together. These letters are very much alike, but the stems are different.

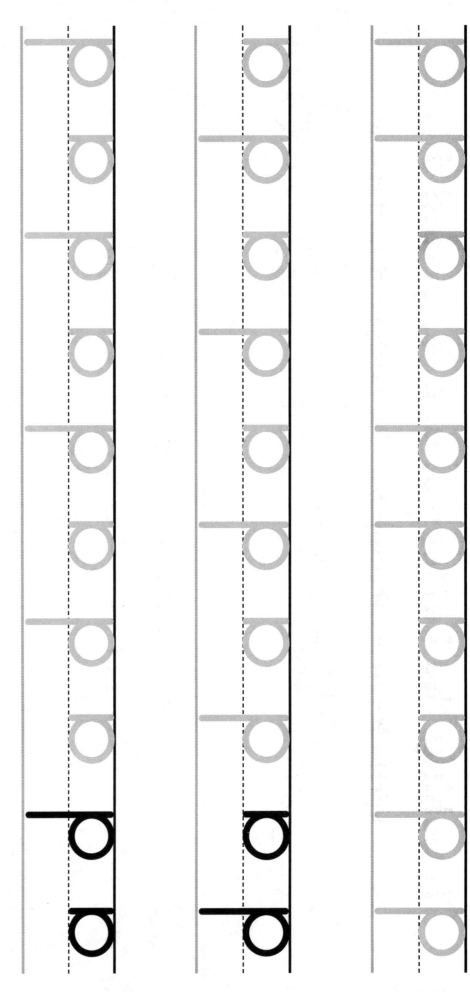

a d a d a d a d a d

d a d a d a d a d a

d d a a d d a a d d

Teaching the Letters o, a, c, e, b, and d *(cont.)*

Write Rhymes Poster for the Letters d and b

d b d

I never mix up d and b
Because it's very funny;
d looks like a silly duck,
And b looks like a bunny.

b d b

Teaching the Letters o, a, c, e, b, and d *(cont.)*

Next to the letter **d**, there is a new letter. The new letter looks very much like the letter **d**. But it is different. It is the letter **b**. Can you see how **d** and **b** are different?

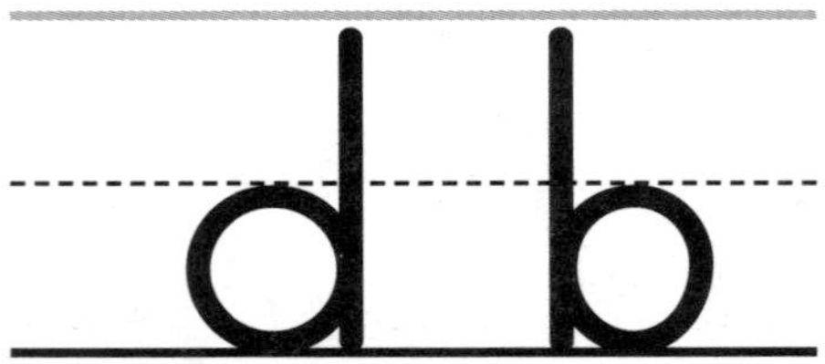

When you make the letter **b**, the line, or stem, comes first. When you made the letters **a** and **d** the circle came first.

To make the letter **b**, make a long line from the light top guide line all the way to the dark bottom guide line. Then make a circle from the dotted middle guide line to the dark bottom guide line. The left side of the circle should touch the long line, or the stem.

Try writing the letter **b**.

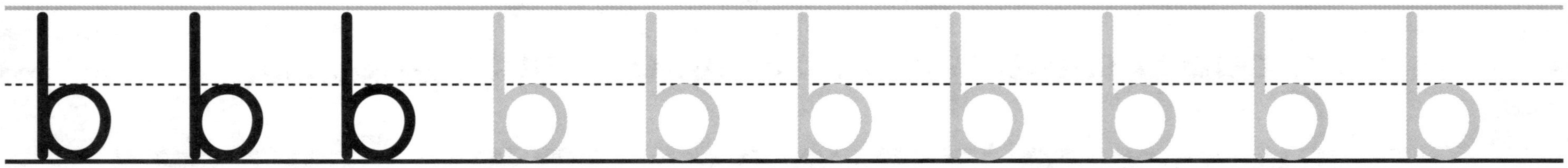

Teaching the Letters o, a, c, e, b, and d *(cont.)*

You can practice writing the letter **b** here. Remember to begin with the long line and then add the circle. Say the name of the letter as you write it.

b b b b b b b b b b

b b b b b b b b b b

b b b b b b b b b b

Teaching the Letters o, a, c, e, b, and d *(cont.)*

Now write the letter **b** all by yourself. Say the name of the letter as you write it.

b b

b b

b b

b b

Teaching the Letters o, a, c, e, b, and d *(cont.)*

Here is a page for you to practice writing the letters **b** and **d** together. Can you tell which one is which? Say the name of each letter as you write it.

d d d d d b b b b b

d b d b d b d b d b

b d b d b d b d b d

Section 1

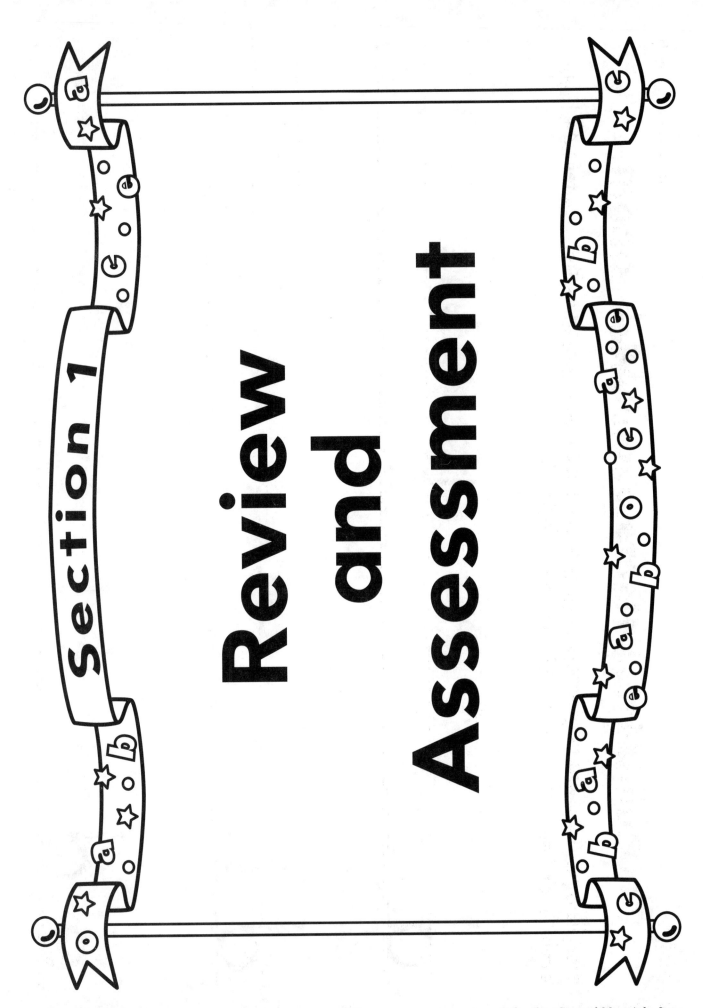

Review and Assessment

Cumulative Review and Assessment

Here is a page for you to practice some of the letters that are made with circles. The letters are **o**, **c**, and **e**.

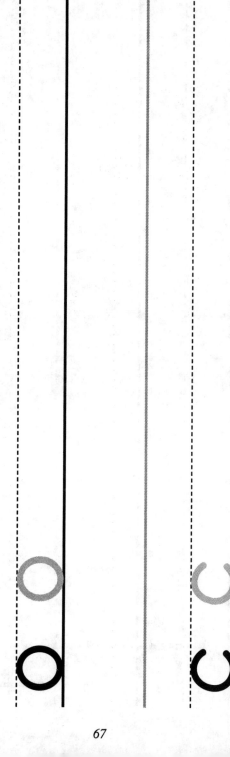

o o

c c

e e

Cumulative Review and Assessment *(cont.)*

Now you can practice the letters that are made with circles and stems. These letters are **a, b,** **and d.**

a a

b b

d d

Cumulative Review and Assessment *(cont.)*

Now let's mix up the letters you know! See if you can make all of them! Say the name of each letter as you write it.

a	d	e	b
d	b	c	e
o	c	a	d
b	o	c	e

Cumulative Review and Assessment *(cont.)*

Here are some more letters to practice. Try your very best. Make all the letters slowly and carefully. Remember to say the name of each letter as you write it.

d	e	b	o
e	a	d	c
b	o	c	a

Cumulative Review and Assessment *(cont.)*

Section 1

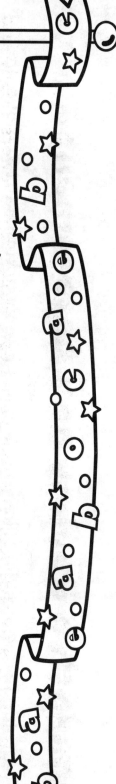

Go back and look at the last four pages you have done. Find the very best **o** that you made. Pick the roundest and neatest **o** that sits perfectly on the guide lines. Draw a circle around it with a bright-colored crayon. Show your perfect letter to your teacher.

Do the same with the letter **a**. Is the stem neat and straight and does it touch the circle on the right side just as it should?

Now do the letter **c** and look for the one that has a perfect stopping and starting place. Then do the letter **e**. Make sure the one you pick has a little line that connects to the **c** part of the letter **e**.

Next, find your very best **d** and **b**. See if the stems on the letters **b** and **d** are straight and tall and go all the way to the light top guide line.

Do any of your letters need extra practice? You can use a piece of Ghost Paper (pages 260, 261, 262, 263, 264, 274) to practice these letters. When you are proud of all your letters, you are ready to go on to the next part of the review.

Cumulative Review and Assessment *(cont.)*

Tani has been learning her letters, just like you. She has been working hard to make each letter neatly and to put the circles and lines in just the right place. She remembers to sit tall, keep her feet on the floor, and to hold her pencil and her paper the right way.

Tani is proud of what she has learned.

Tani wrote the letter **o**.

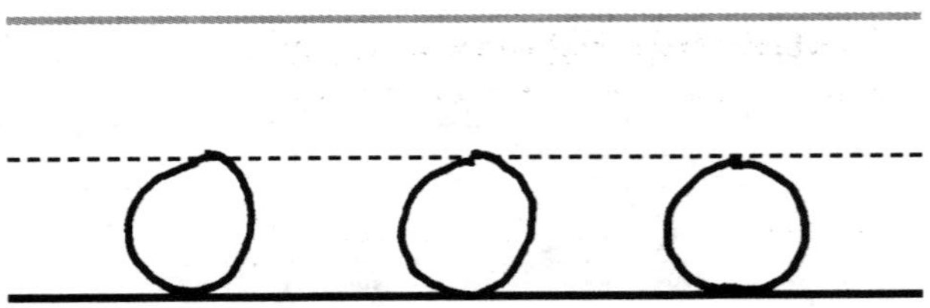

Now, you write the letter **o**.

How do you think they look? Are they neat? Are they made exactly right?

Cumulative Review and Assessment *(cont.)*

Tani has made more letters here. You can make some, too.

Tani wrote the letter a.

a a a

Now, you write the letter a.

Tani wrote the letter c.

c c c

Now, you write the letter c.

Tani wrote the letter e.

e e e

Now, you write the letter e.

Tani wrote the letter d.

d d d

Now, you write the letter d.

Tani wrote the letter b.

b b b

Now, you write the letter b.

Cumulative Review and Assessment *(cont.)*

Section 1

Now you know six letters of the alphabet! You know their names, and you know how to write each one.

You already know that letters can be put together to make words. You have helped to make some words by tracing letters.

You know so many letters now that you can write whole words!

On the next two pages you will find some words that you can write. There are not any lines for you to trace because you know how to make all the letters! Your teacher will read each word to you. Then you will write the word all by yourself. Take your time, and do your very best! The words of the songs you learned will help you remember how to make each letter.

Get ready to show off!

Cumulative Review and Assessment *(cont.)*

Write these words.

add add

cob cob

doe doe

bob bob

Cumulative Review and Assessment *(cont.)*

Write these words.

bed	bed
odd	odd
cab	cab
dab	dab

Section 2

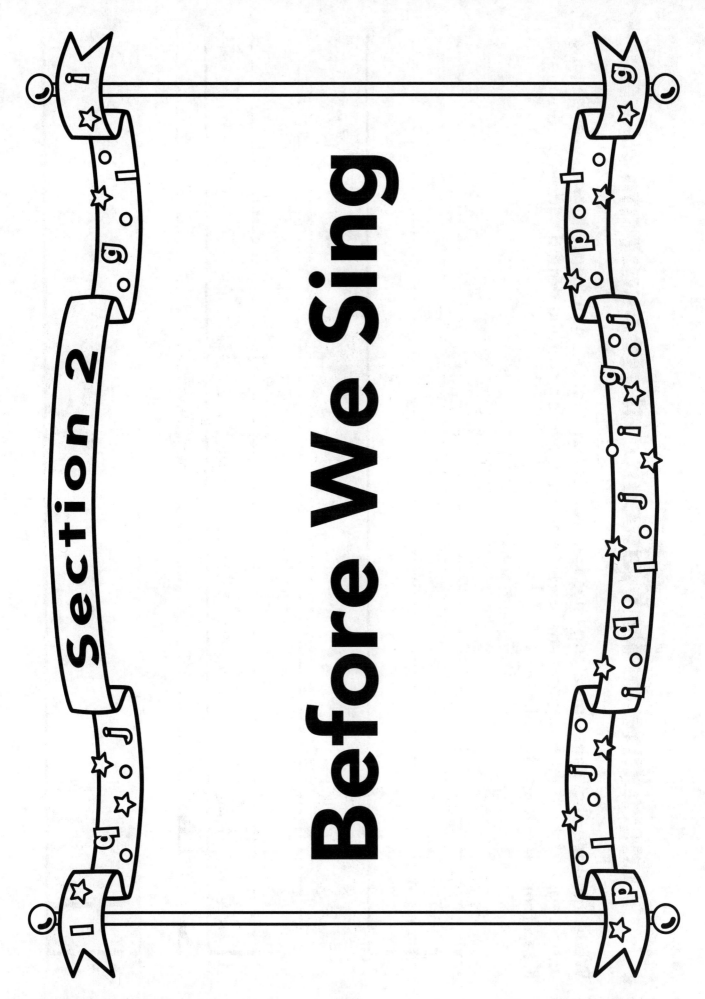

Before We Sing

Long and Short Lines and Hook Strokes

We have made short lines and long lines before. Let's practice some here. Make sure the long lines begin at the light top guide line and the short lines begin at the dotted middle guide line. Keep them neat and straight.

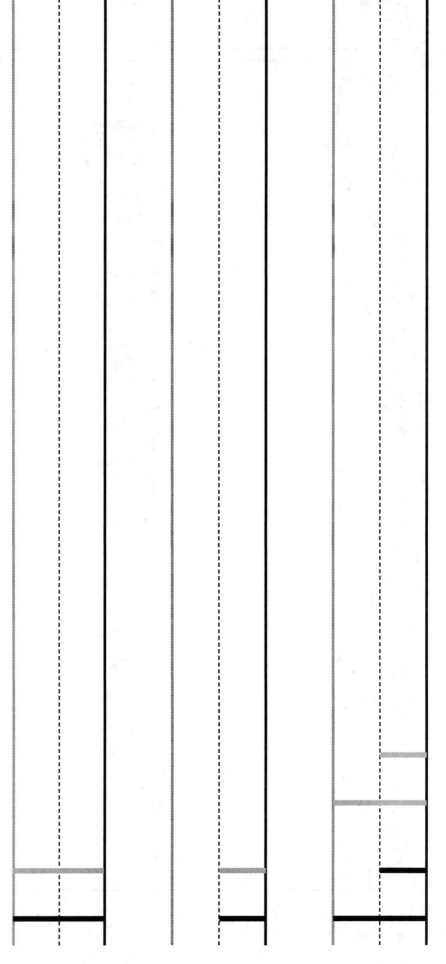

Long and Short Lines and Hook Strokes *(cont.)*

Many shapes can be made with straight lines. Sometimes the lines do not go up and down. Sometimes the lines go sideways!

Can you make some chairs?

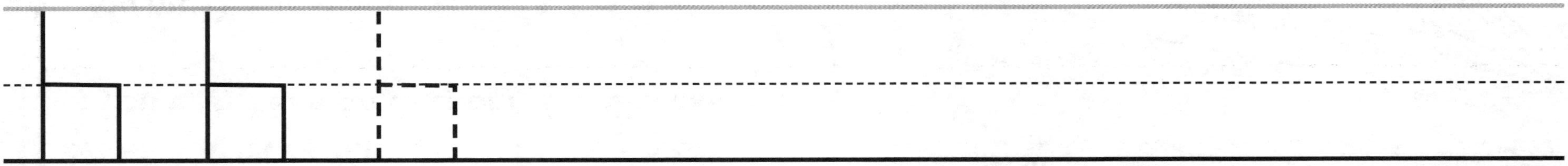

Can you make some birthday candles?

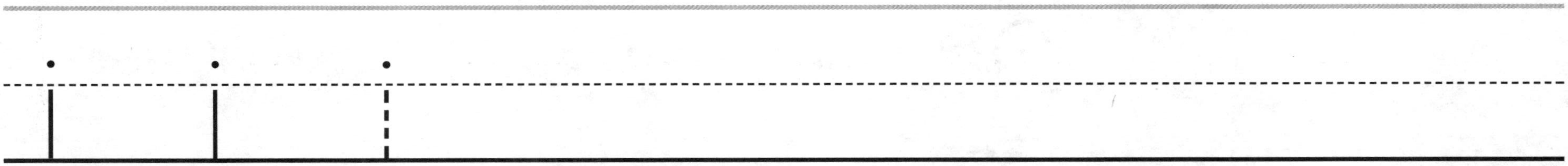

Can you make some little squares?

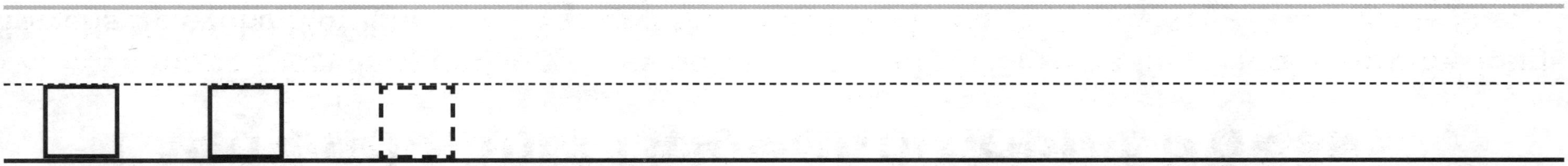

Long and Short Lines and Hook Strokes *(cont.)*

Here is a new kind of line.

It begins like a straight line, but it curves at the bottom.

It can curve this way. Or it can curve this way.

It is a **hook**. Have you ever seen a fishhook? It looks like this.

Have you ever seen an anchor? It looks like this.

Can you make some hooks?

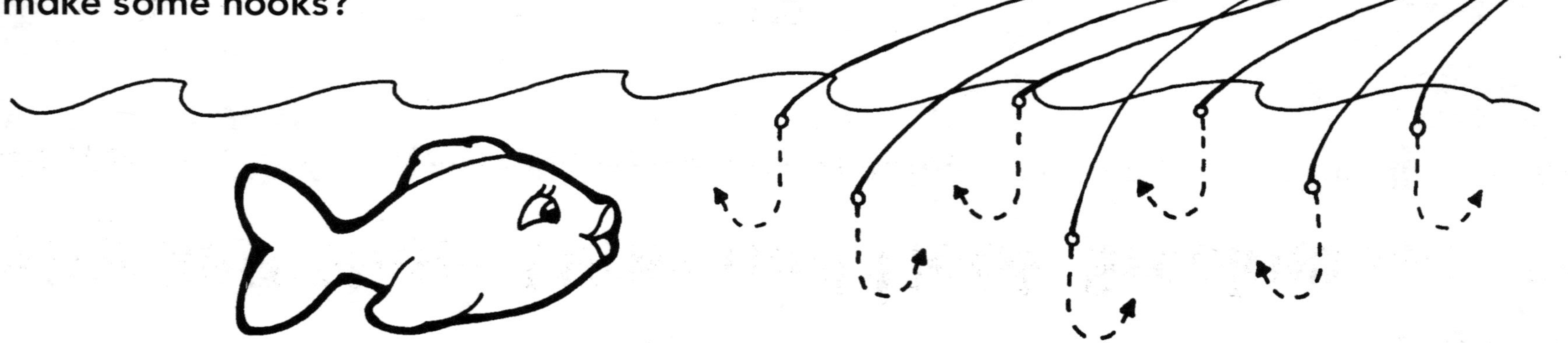

Long and Short Lines and Hook Strokes *(cont.)*

The handle of an umbrella sometimes looks like a hook.

It can go his way.

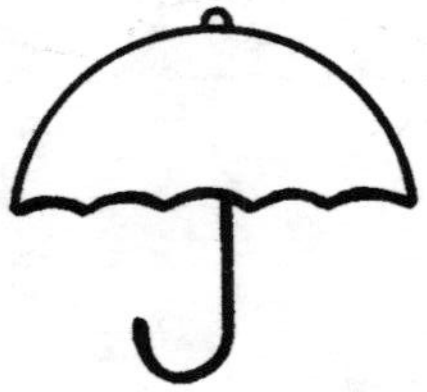

Or it can
go this way.

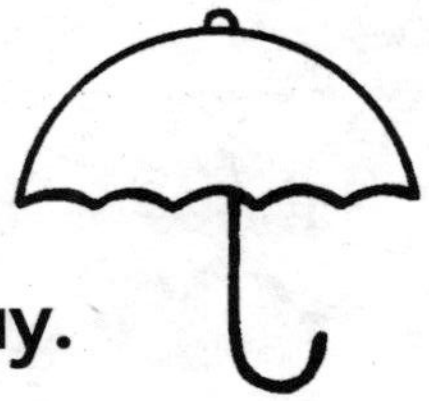

Can you make some umbrella handles that look like hooks?

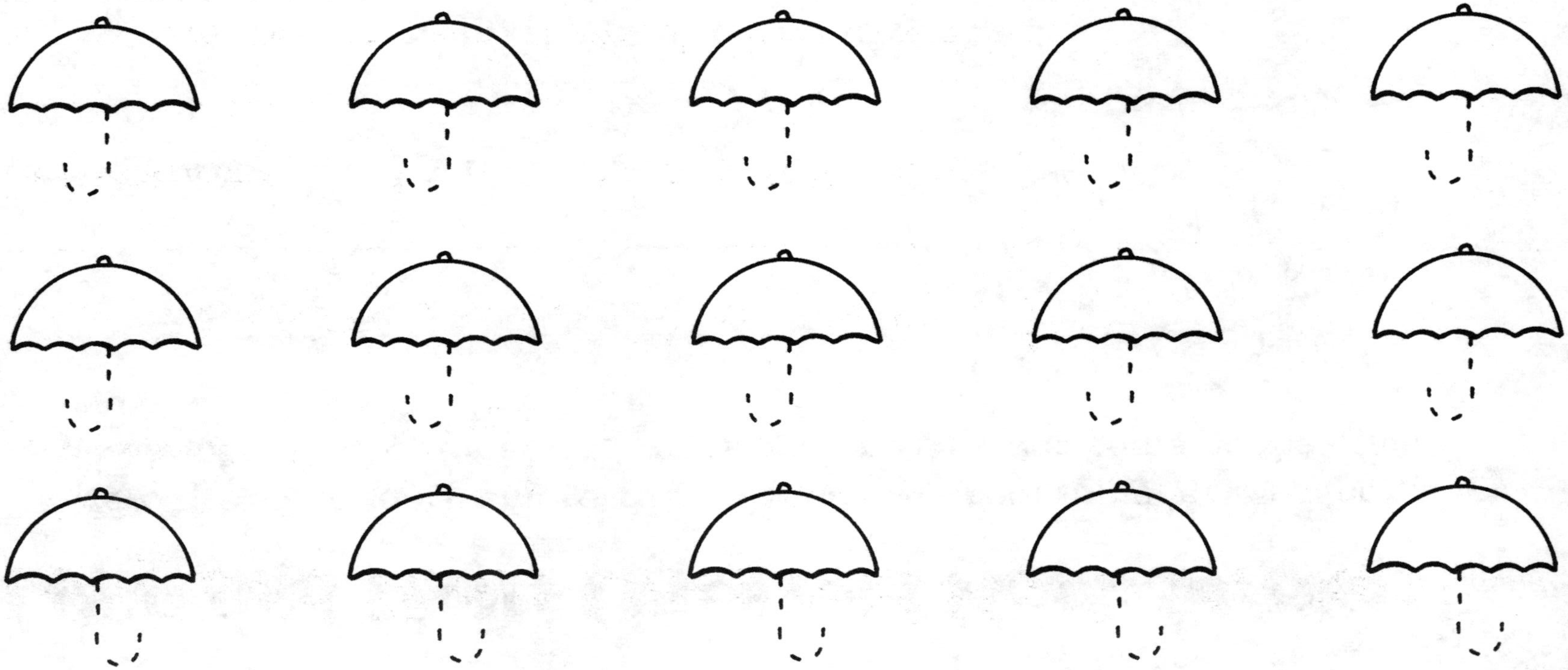

Long and Short Lines and Hook Strokes *(cont.)*

Here are some fancy umbrellas. Can you give them some handles that look like **hooks**? Make some of the hooks go one way and some go the other way.

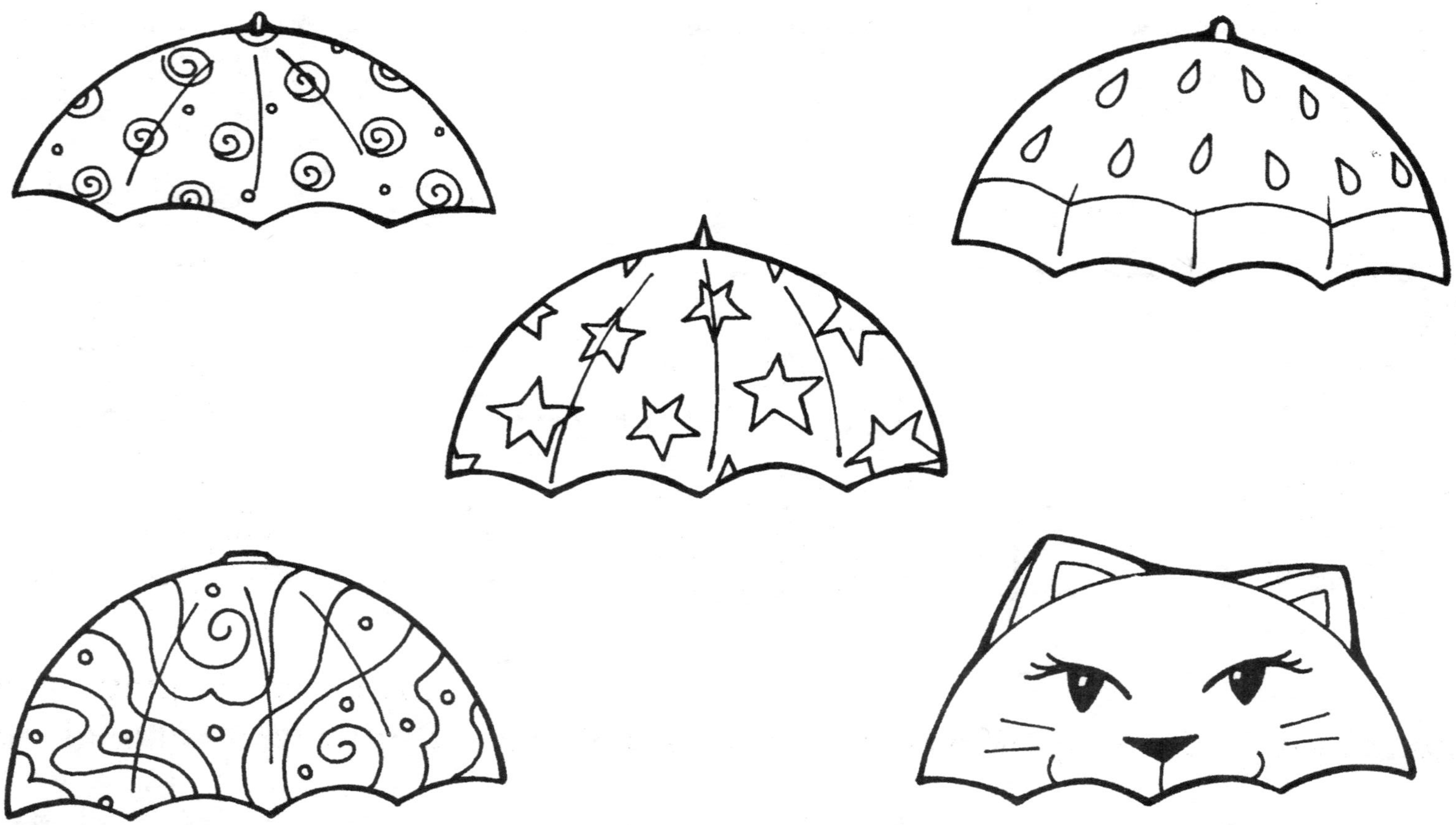

Long and Short Lines and Hook Strokes *(cont.)*

There are animals that have tails that are shaped like a hook. Some are real animals like a seahorse, a monkey, and a cat.

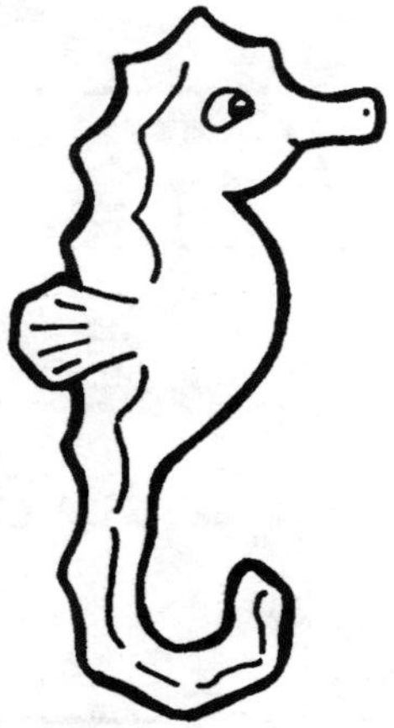

Some are pretend animals, like these.

Long and Short Lines and Hook Strokes *(cont.)*

Let's practice some of those hooks on the guide lines. You can make big hooks that go this way.

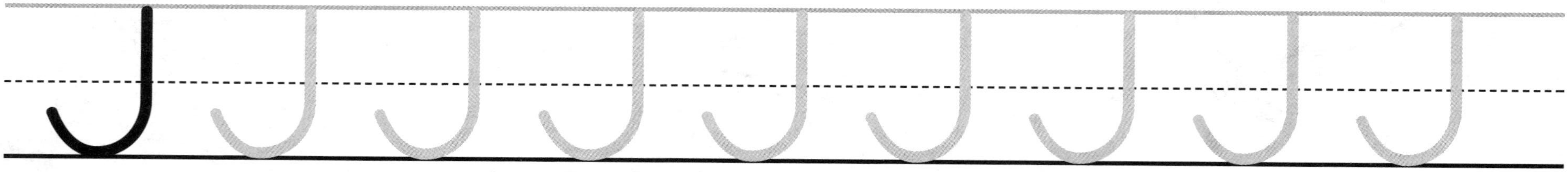

Or you can make big hooks that go this way.

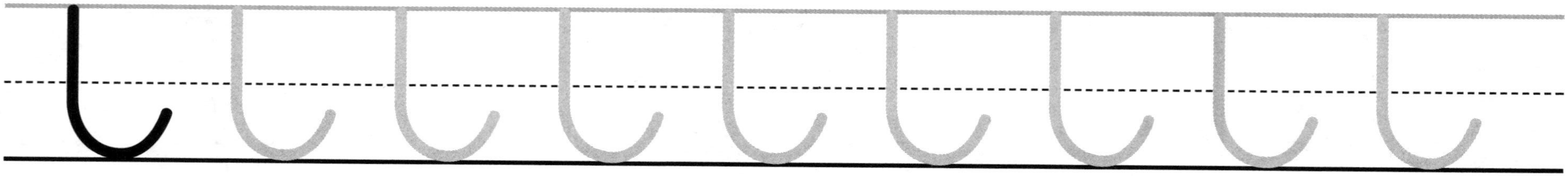

You can make small hooks that go either way.

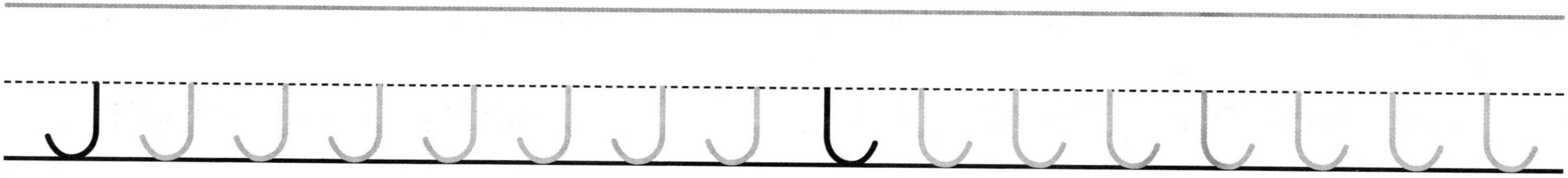

Long and Short Lines and Hook Strokes *(cont.)*

Sometimes hooks can go **under** the guide lines!

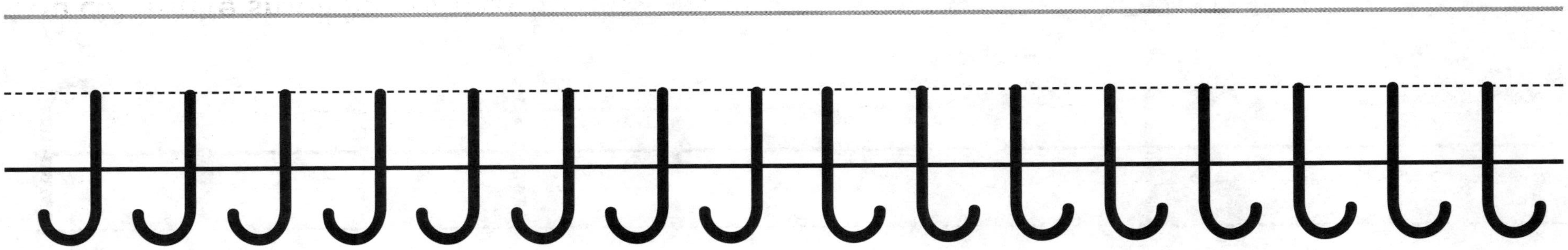

Do you remember the seahorse? It hangs its tail underneath the dark bottom guide line! It hangs its tail down in the water, where the fishhooks go!

Can you make some hooks that go **under** the dark bottom guide line?

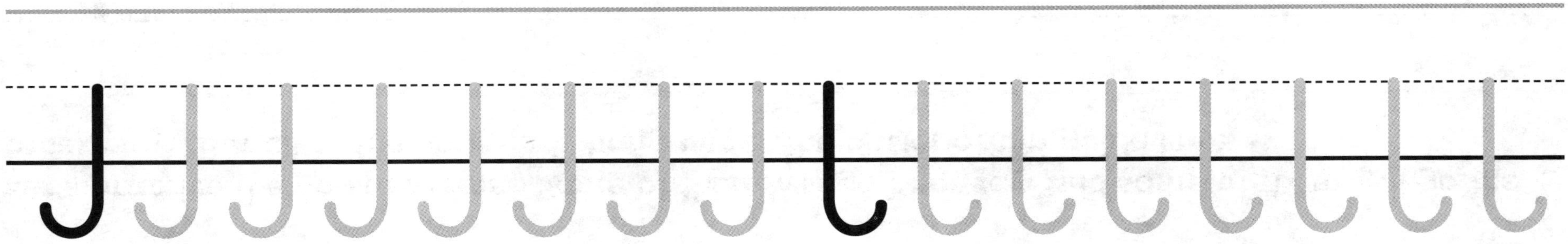

Long and Short Lines and Hook Strokes *(cont.)*

Let's practice the hook strokes. Some of them will go one way, and some of them will go the other way. But all of the hooks will hang under the dark bottom guide line!

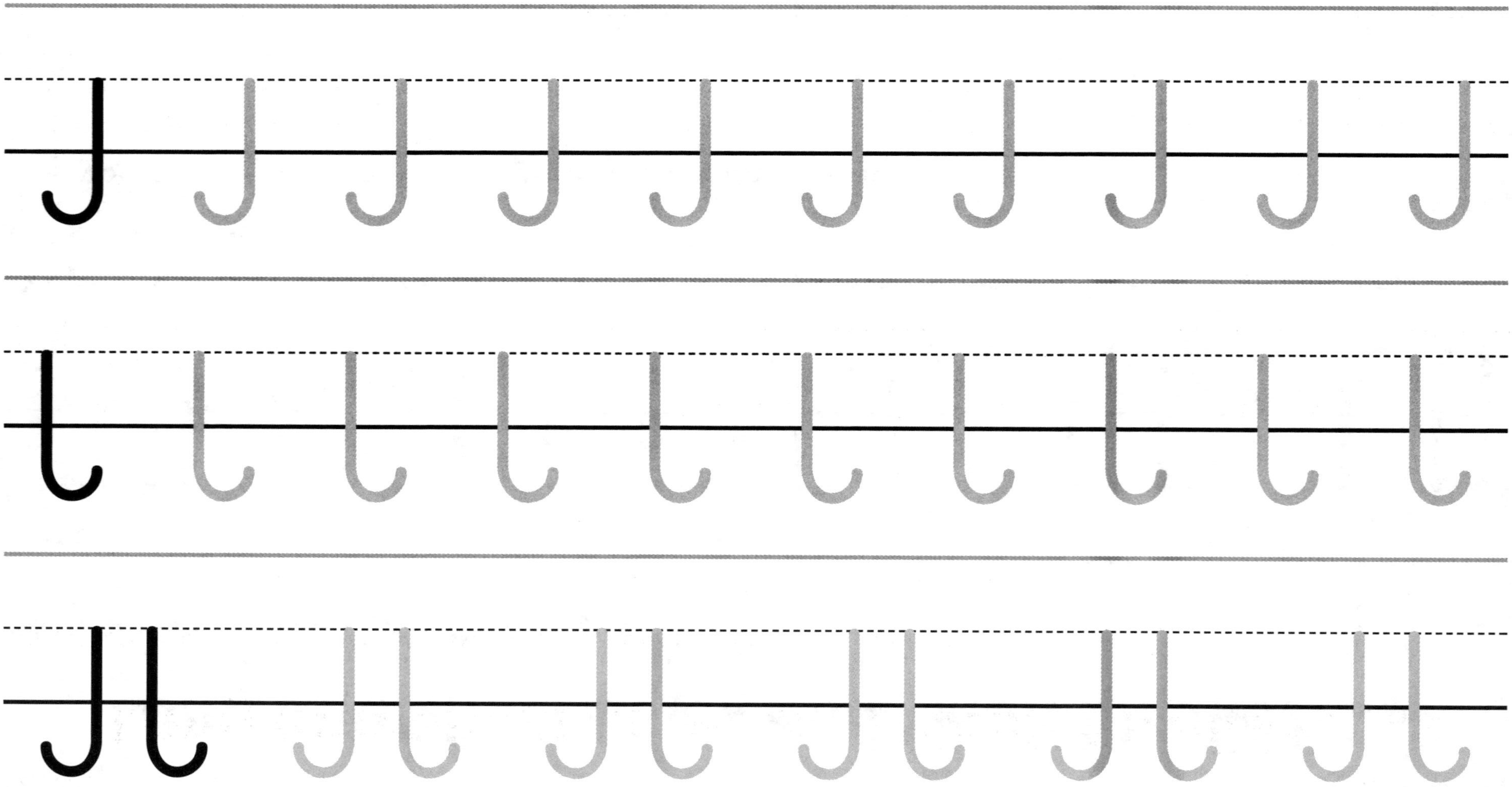

Long and Short Lines and Hook Strokes *(cont.)*

Here is a page to practice making the hook stroke all by yourself!

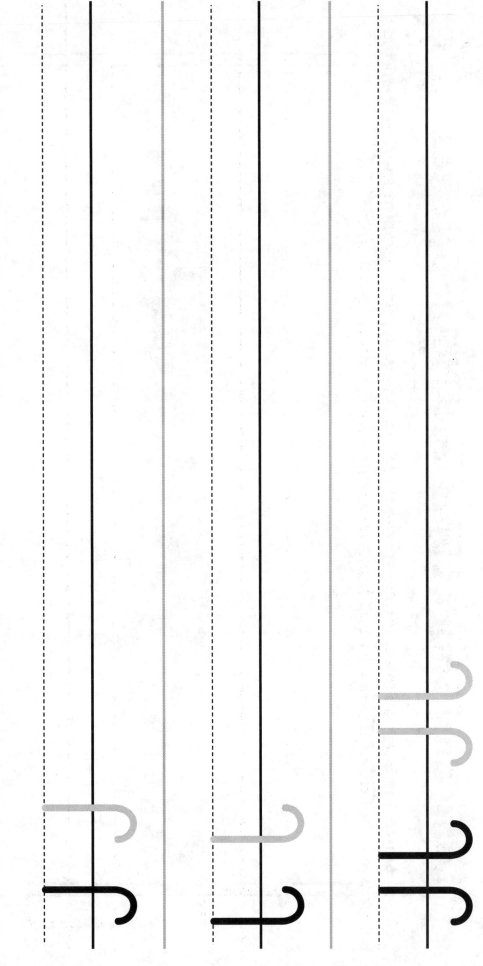

Section 2

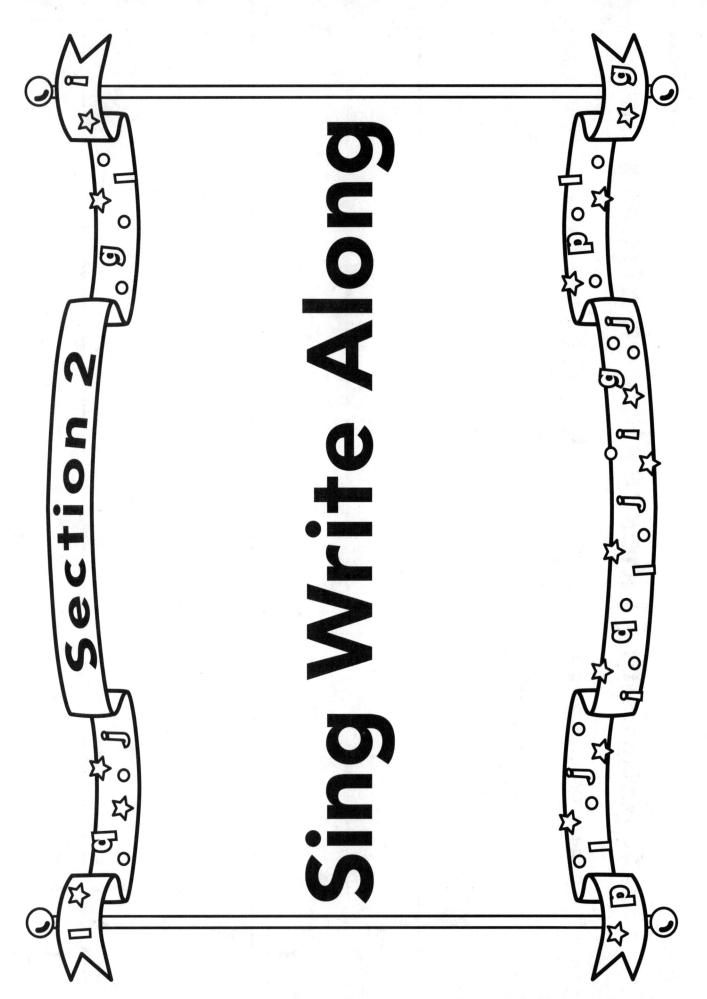

Sing Write Along

Teaching the Letters l, i, j, g, q, and p

Write Rhymes Poster for the Letter l

A long line downward from the top
I'm sure that you can tell,
This is an easy one to do.
It is the letter l.

Teaching the Letters l, i, j, g, q, and p *(cont.)*

Here is a surprise! You have already made many long, straight lines.

A long straight line makes a letter of the alphabet! It is the letter l.

Practice writing the letter l here. Say the name of the letter as you write it.

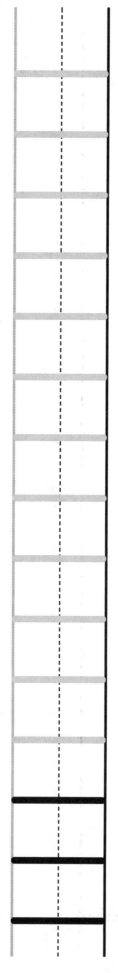

Do you remember how the circle shape was exactly the same as the letter **o**? This straight line is exactly the same as the letter l. One is a shape and the other is a letter. But there is not any difference in the way they look, and you will make them exactly the same way.

Teaching the Letters l, i, j, g, q, and p *(cont.)*

Here is a page to practice making those long, straight lines you can make so well! But now you will call them by their letter name, l. Remember to say the name of the letter as you write it.

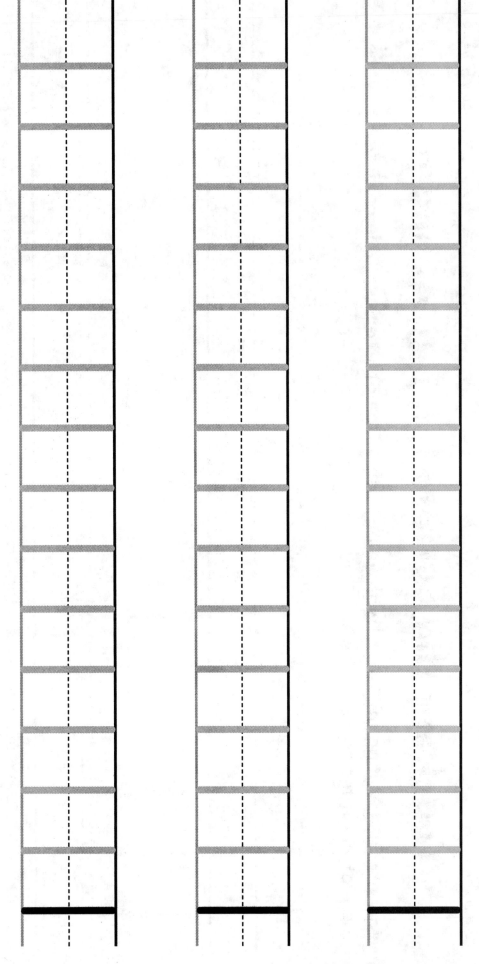

Teaching the Letters l, i, j, g, q, and p *(cont.)*

Now practice writing the letter l without any help. Do not let an l wobble or curve! Say the name of the letter as you write it.

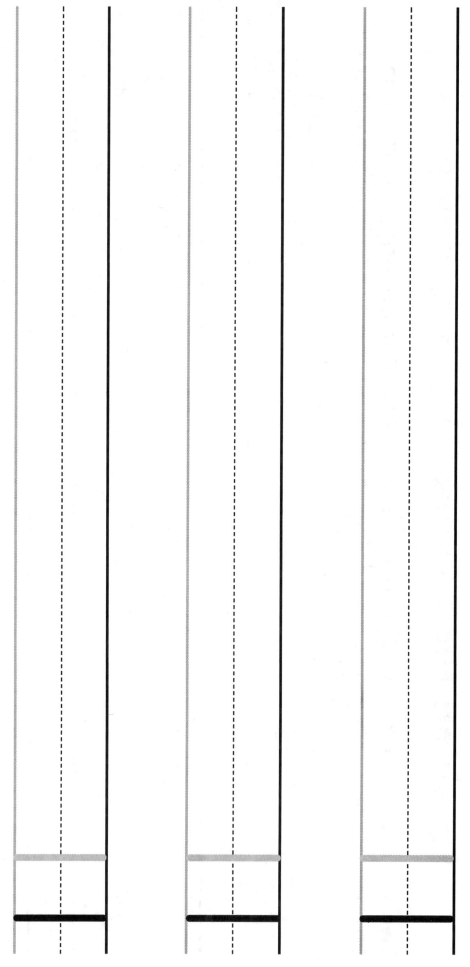

Is each l straight and tall?

Teaching the Letters l, i, j, g, q, and p *(cont.)*

Write Rhymes Poster for the Letter i

i i i

Pull a line down, keep it straight,
Don't make it reach too high.
Then put a dot above its head,
It is the letter i.

i i i

Teaching the Letters l, i, j, g, q, and p *(cont.)*

Here is a birthday cake with some candles. The candles are very special. Each candle is a short, straight line with a dot. The dot is in the middle of the upper space. It is halfway between the dotted middle guide line and the light top guide line.

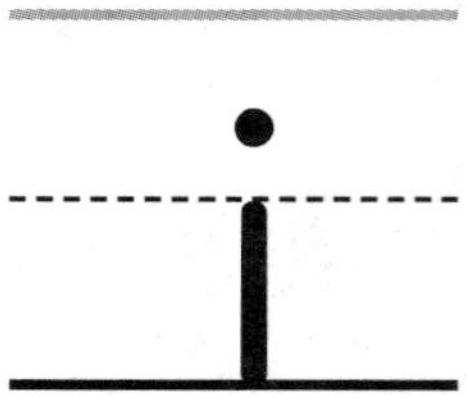

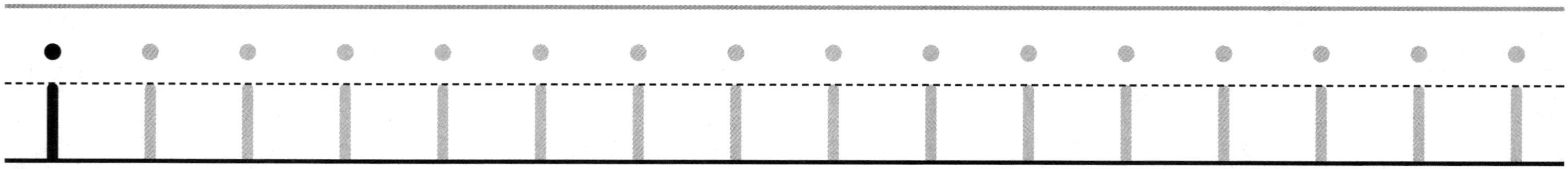

Each little line has its own neat dot just above it. The little line with the dot makes the letter i!

Teaching the Letters l, i, j, g, q, and p *(cont.)*

Practice making some dots here. A dot is just like the caterpillar's eye. Put it in just the right place! It goes between the dotted middle guide line and the light top guide line. Can you find just the right spot for the dots?

Now, practice putting that little dot over a short, straight line.

You have made the letter i!

Teaching the Letters l, i, j, g, q, and p *(cont.)*

Write the letter i all by yourself. Be sure to say the name of the letter as you write it.

i i

i i

i i

i i

Teaching the Letters l, i, j, g, q, and p *(cont.)*

Now let's mix up the new letters l and i.

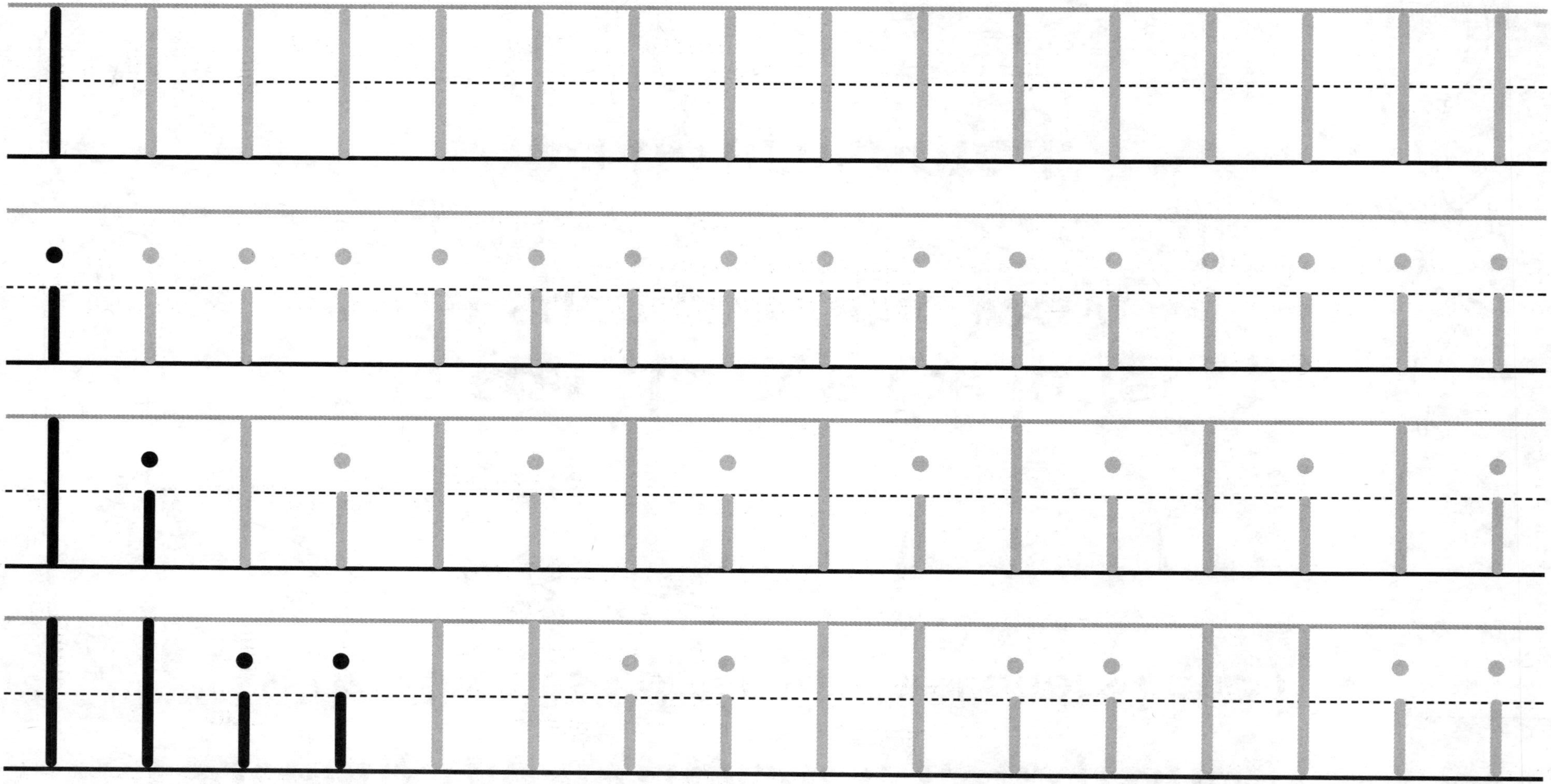

Is each l straight and tall? Does each i have a neat dot?

Teaching the Letters l, i, j, g, q, and p *(cont.)*

Write Rhymes Poster for the Letters i and j

i j i

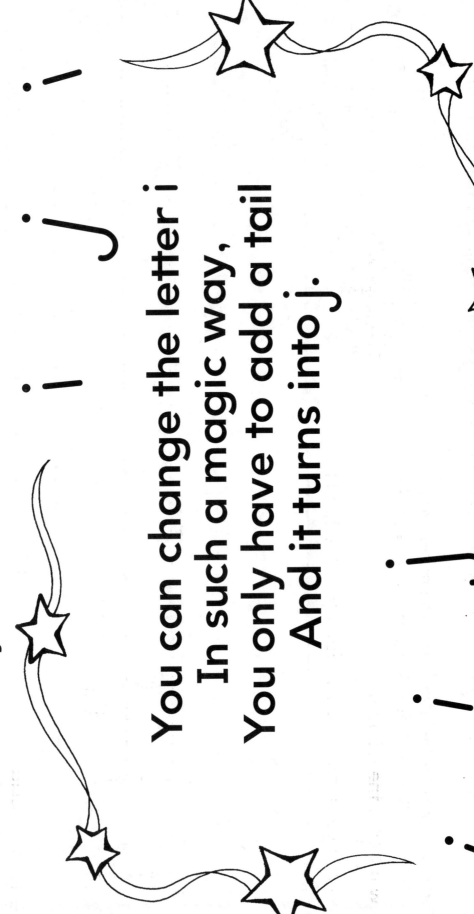

You can change the letter i
In such a magic way,
You only have to add a tail
And it turns into j.

j i j

Teaching the Letters l, i, j, g, q, and p *(cont.)*

Our song tells us the story of our new letter. It begins just like the letter i, but it has a tail! The new letter is the letter j.

Do you see something special about the tail on the letter j?

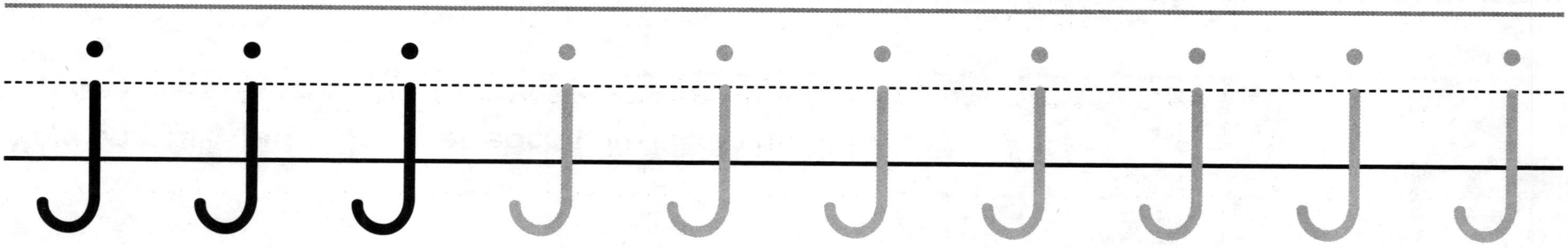

The tail is special because it has a hook, just like the umbrella handles you made. This hook goes down under the dark bottom guide line and curves toward the beginning side of your paper. The tail on the letter j hangs in the water!

Teaching the Letters l, i, j, g, q, and p *(cont.)*

Let's practice writing the letter j. First, make a straight line that starts at the dotted middle guide line and goes under the dark bottom guide line. Carefully add an umbrella hook to the bottom of the line. Make sure the hook is under the dark bottom guide line. Curve the hook toward the beginning side of your paper.

Now carefully put a dot over each j, just like you did with the letter i.

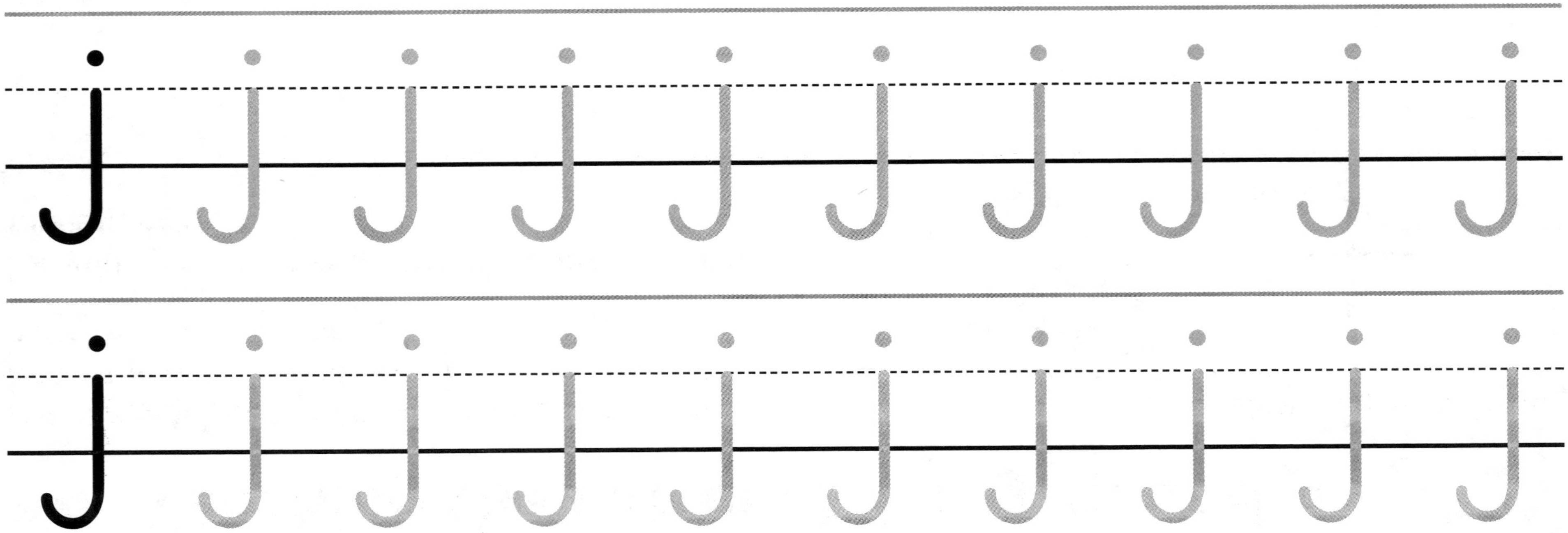

Teaching the Letters l, i, j, g, q, and p *(cont.)*

Here is a page for you to practice writing the letter j. Say the name of the letter as you write it.

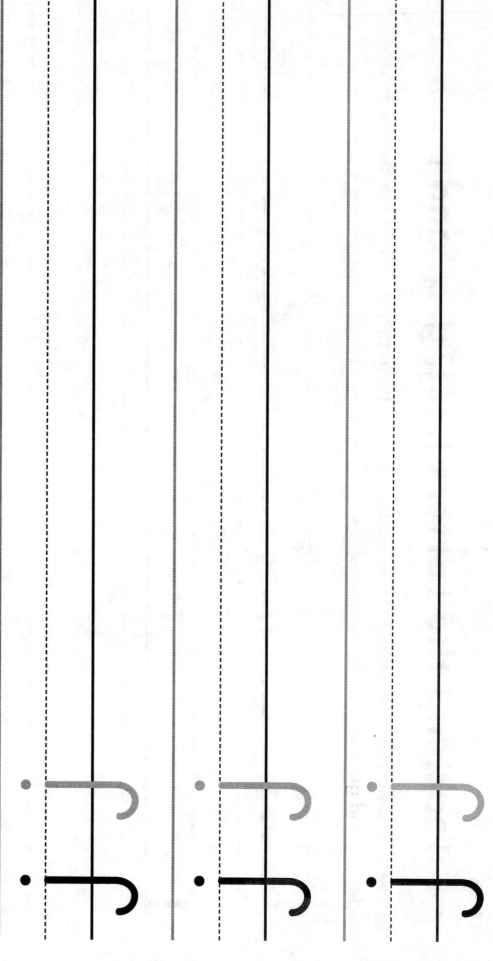

j j

j j

j j

Teaching the Letters l, i, j, g, q, and p *(cont.)*

Now let's mix up the three new letters, l, i, and j. Say the name of each letter as you write it.

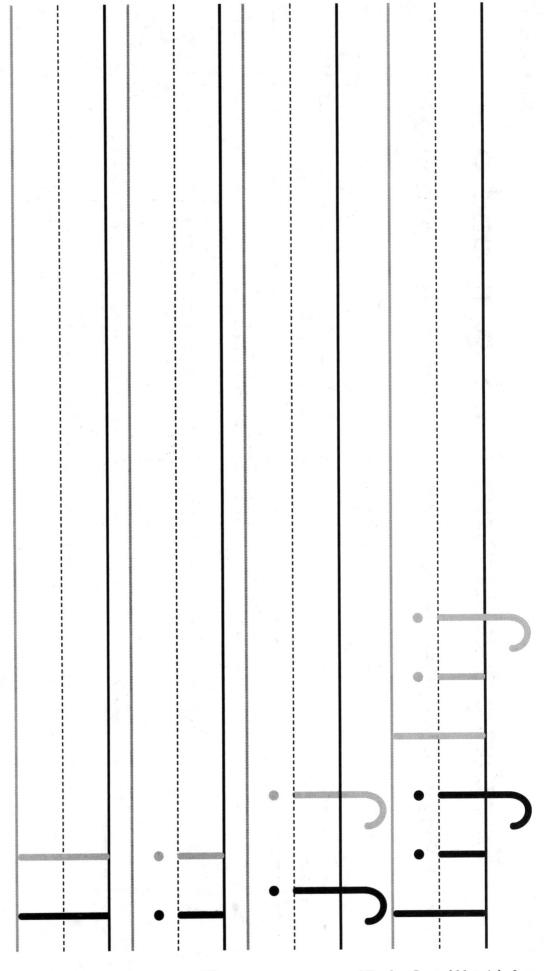

l l

i i

j j

l i j l i j

Teaching the Letters l, i, j, g, q, and p *(cont.)*

Write Rhymes Poster for the Letters g, j, p, and q

g j q p

g and j and p and q
Their tails are really great.
Two curl back and one curls front
And one just hangs there straight.

j q g p

Teaching the Letters l, i, j, g, q, and p *(cont.)*

Here are three more creatures with tails that hang in the water. One has a tail that curves the same way as the letter j. This is Gus, the cat.

Queek, the monkey, has a tail that curves the other way. And Percival Possum has a tail that hangs in the water, too. But his tail does not curve at all! His tail just hangs down straight!

Now let's look at these creatures and the letters they make.

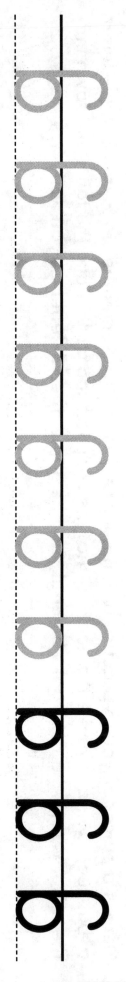

Teaching the Letters l, i, j, g, q, and p *(cont.)*

Let's look at the cat first. Gus's letter, which is called g, begins with a circle, just like the letter **o**. Then you will add a short, straight line on the right side of the circle, as if you were writing the letter **a**. But don't stop! Keep going down under the dark bottom guide line and add a tail. Curve the tail the same way as the letter **j**, toward the beginning side of your paper.

g

g g g g g g g g g g

Teaching the Letters l, i, j, g, q, and p *(cont.)*

Here is a place for you to practice writing our new letter, **g**. Remember to begin with the letter **a**, but keep going to make the hook so that the cat's tail can curl. Make the tail hang down into the water where the fish hooks belong! Say the name of each letter as you write it.

g g g g g g g g g g

g g g g g g g g g g

g g g g g g g g g g

Teaching the Letters l, i, j, g, q, and p *(cont.)*

Now practice writing the letter g all by yourself. Say the name of the letter as you write it.

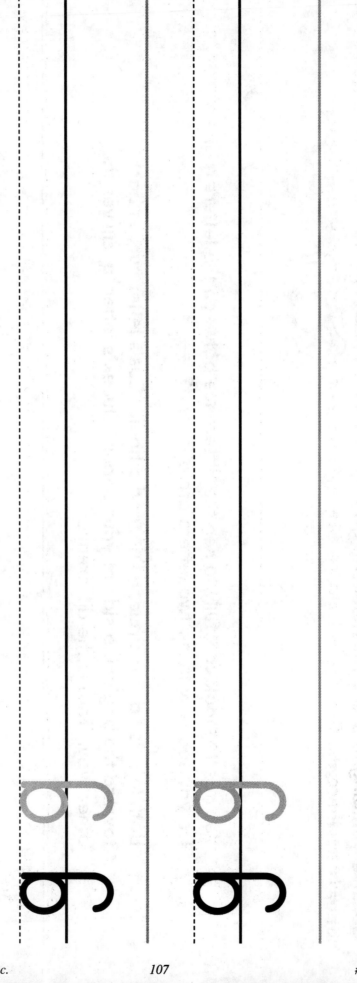

g g

g g

g g

Teaching the Letters l, i, j, g, q, and p *(cont.)*

Queek, the monkey, has a letter that looks very much like Gus's **g**. Queek's letter is the letter **q**.

You need to look carefully to see the difference between the letters **g** and **q**. Do you see how these two letters are different?

Both letters have a circle, a line, and a hook. Gus's letter curves back toward the beginning side of your paper. Queek's letter, **q**, curves the other way. That is the difference!

q q q q q q q q q q

Teaching the Letters l, i, j, g, q, and p *(cont.)*

Start the letter **q** by writing the letter **a**. But after you have made the short, straight line, keep right on going. Go under the dark bottom guide line to make the monkey's tail curl in the water. Make sure it curves differently from the cat's tail. Go this way with Queek's tail. →

q q q q q q q q q q

q q q q q q q q q q

q q q q q q q q q q

Teaching the Letters l, i, j, g, q, and p *(cont.)*

Now practice writing the letter q all by yourself. Say the name of the letter as you write it.

q q

q q

q q

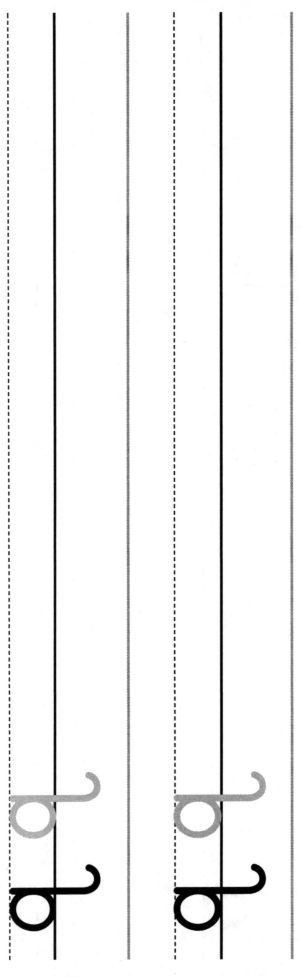

Does the tail curve the way it should?

Teaching the Letters l, i, j, g, q, and p *(cont.)*

Now we will mix up the letters g and q. Can you remember which letter is which? Say the name of each letter as you write it.

g g

q q

g q g q

Teaching the Letters l, i, j, g, q, and p *(cont.)*

Here is the possum, Percival. He has a new kind of tail. His tail does not have a hook. It is just a straight line, but it does hang down in the water!

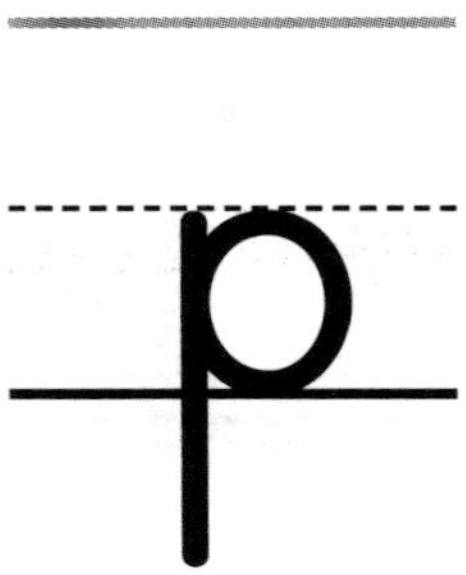

Something is different about the way you will make the possum's letter **p**. When you made **a**, **d**, **g**, and **q**, you made the circle first and then the line. But the letter **p** is like the letter **b**. You will make the line, or stem, first. Then you will make the circle.

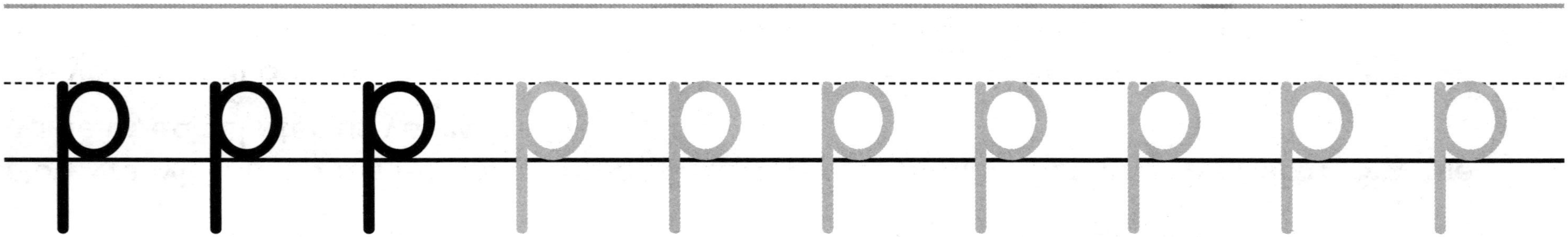

Teaching the Letters l, i, j, g, q, and p *(cont.)*

To write the letter **p**, begin with your pencil on the dotted middle guide line. Pull down to the dark bottom guide line and go under it. Go straight into the water to make the possum's tail. Lift your pencil and go back to the top of the line you just made. Make your circle next to the line. The top of the circle should touch the dotted middle guide line, and the bottom of the circle should touch the dark bottom guide line.

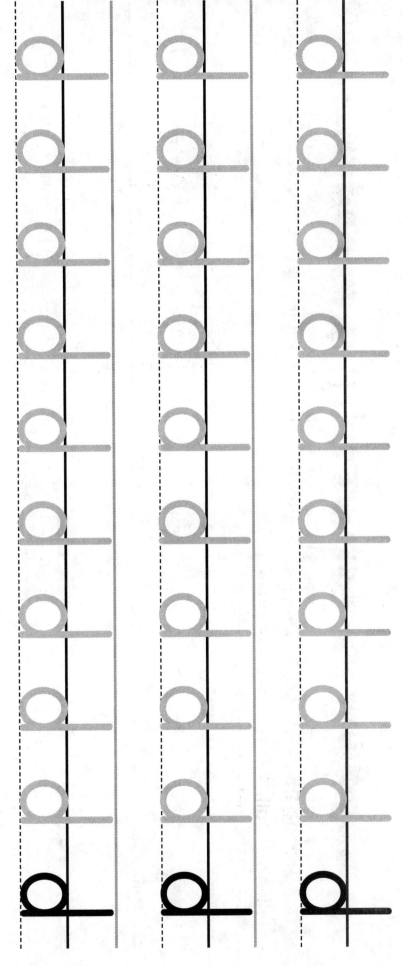

p p p p p p p p p p

p p p p p p p p p p

p p p p p p p p p p

Teaching the Letters l, i, j, g, q, and p *(cont.)*

Now try writing the letter **p** by yourself. Remember that this tail does not curve at all! Say the name of the letter as you write it.

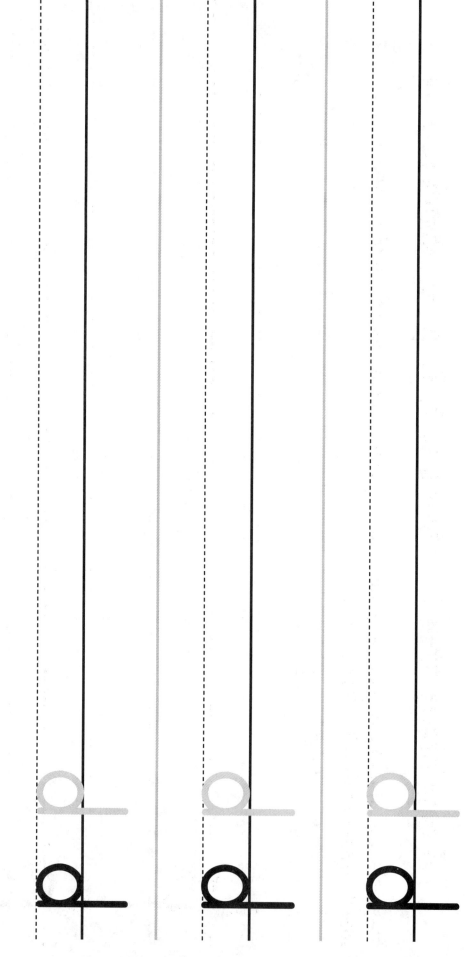

p p

p p

p p

Teaching the Letters l, i, j, g, q, and p *(cont.)*

The letters **g**, **q**, and **p** are all very much alike. Can you say the name of each one as you practice these three letters?

g g

q q

p p

Teaching the Letters l, i, j, g, q, and p *(cont.)*

Now let's write the letters **j**, **g**, and **q**. All these letters have tails that hang down in the water. Say the name of each letter as you write it.

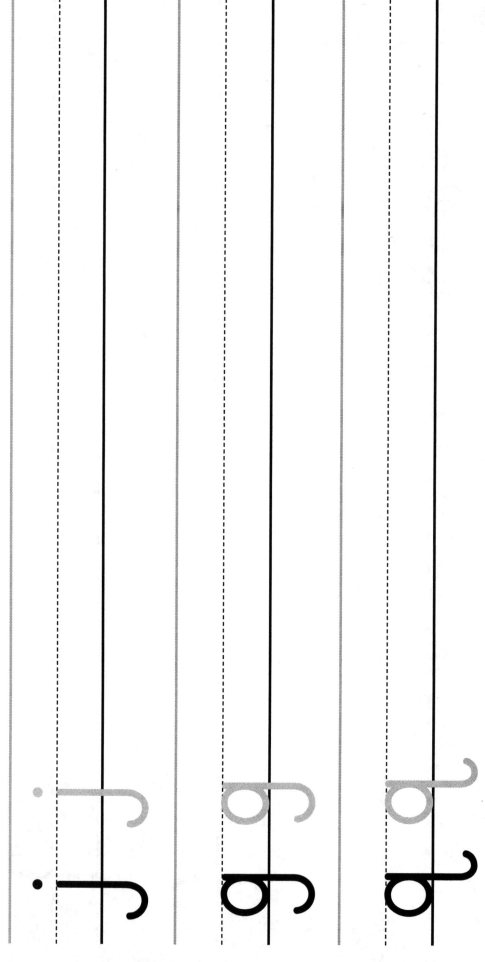

j j

g g

q q

Teaching the Letters l, i, j, g, q, and p *(cont.)*

Now we will add the letter i to all the other letters you have been practicing. Remember to make a small, neat dot on the letters j and i.

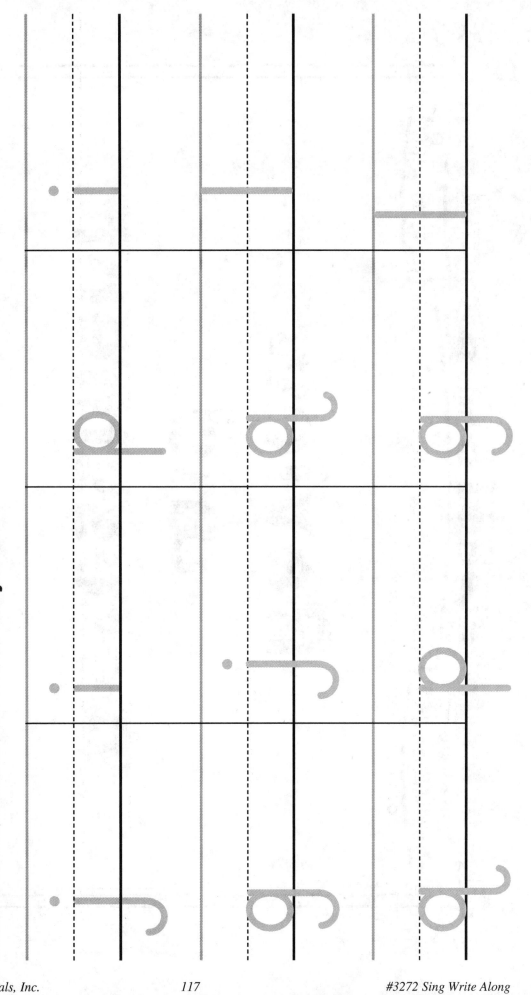

j	i	p	i
g	j	q	l
q	p	g	l

Section 2

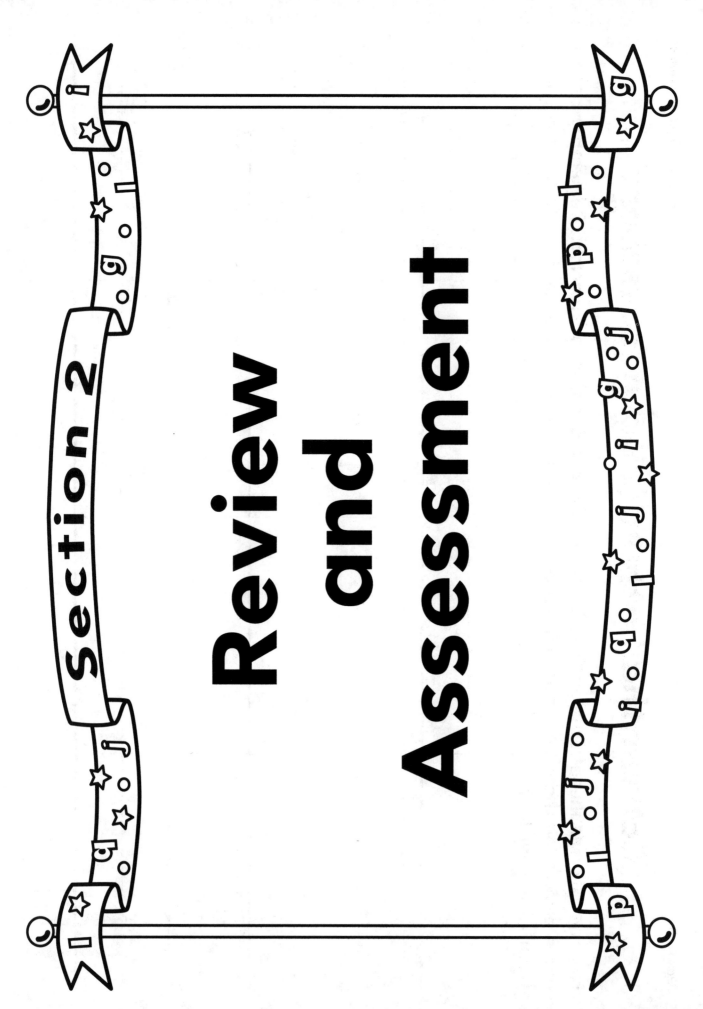

Review and Assessment

Cumulative Review and Assessment

Here are the letters for Gus (**g**), Queek (**q**), and Percival (**p**). They all have tails that hang down in the water. They are very much alike. Write the letters **g**, **q**, and **p**. Say the name of each letter as you write it.

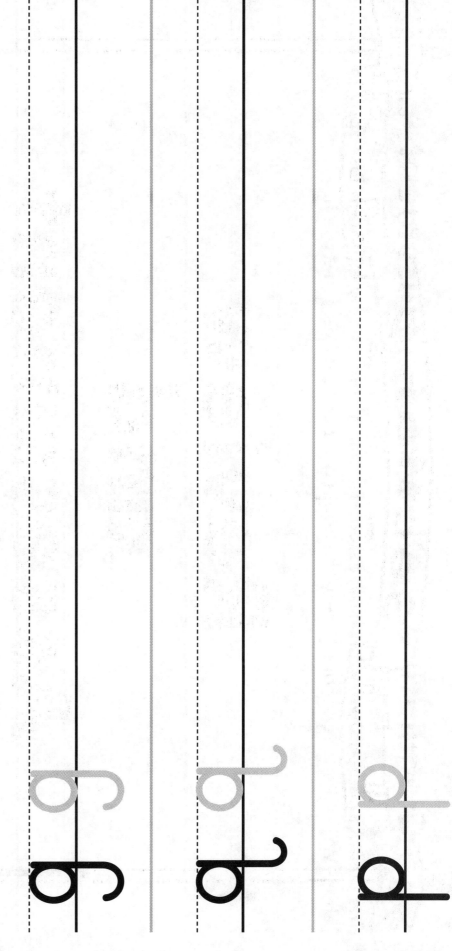

g g

q q

p p

Cumulative Review and Assessment *(cont.)*

The letters i and j are very much alike, too. Both of them have dots that go just above the letter. Write the letters i and j. Say the name of each letter as you write it.

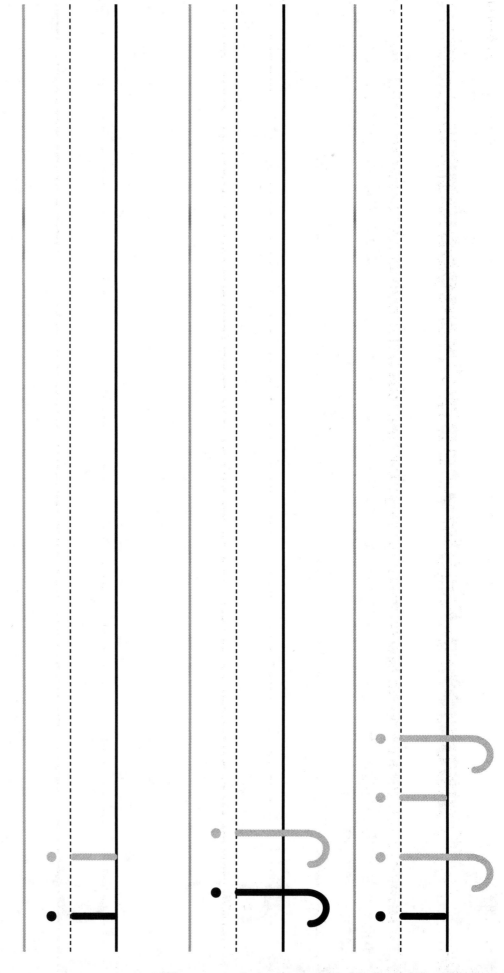

i i

j j

i j i j

Cumulative Review and Assessment *(cont.)*

The letters l, i, and j are all old friends. Can you remember the name of each letter as you write it?

l l

i i

j j

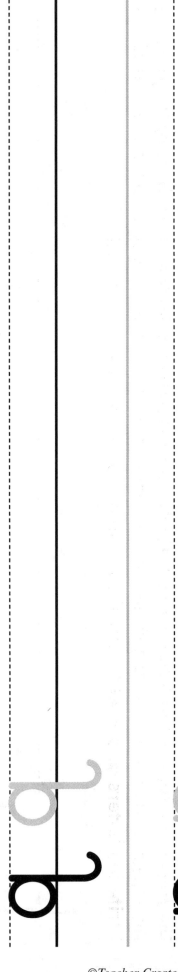

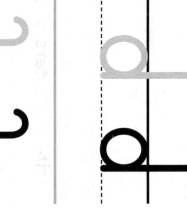

Cumulative Review and Assessment *(cont.)*

The letters **g**, **q**, and **p** are alike, too. Each one of these letters is made with a circle and a straight line that curves to become a tail that hangs down under the dark bottom guide line. Write the letters **g**, **q**, and **p**. Say the name of each letter as you write it.

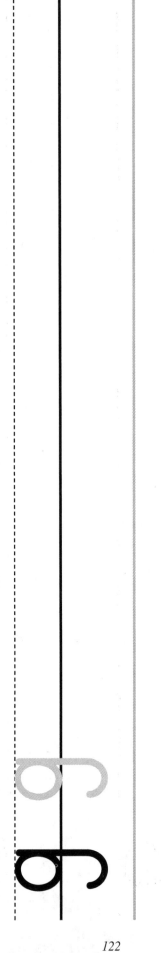

g g

q q

p p

Cumulative Review and Assessment *(cont.)*

Do you remember the letters **o, a,** and **c**? All three of these letters are made with circles. Only the letter a has a short, straight line. Remember the letter **c** has a piece missing from its circle. Write the letters **o, a,** and **c.** Say the name of each letter as you write it.

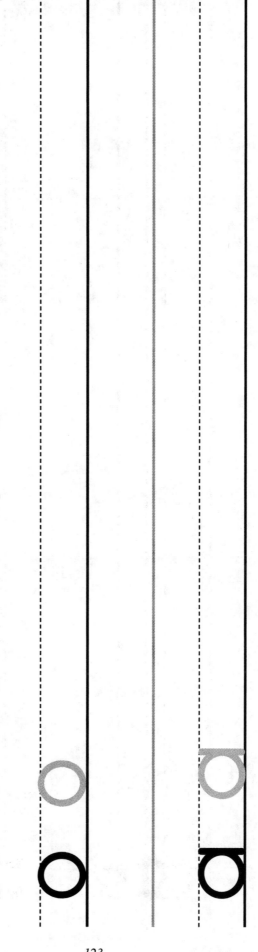

o o

a a

c c

Cumulative Review and Assessment *(cont.)*

The letters **e**, **b**, and **d** belong together, too. To write the letters **e**, **b**, and **d**, you need a circle and a straight line. But the straight line for the letter **e** goes sideways! Write the letters **e**, **b**, and **d**. Say the name of each letter as you write it.

e e

b b

d d

Cumulative Review and Assessment *(cont.)*

Now let's mix up all the letters you know so far! Look how many different letters you can write! Say the name of each letter as you write it.

e	j	q	c
b	p	a	g
i	o	d	l

Cumulative Review and Assessment *(cont.)*

Here are some more mixed up letters. Write all these letters slowly and carefully, and do your very best. Remember to say the name of each letter as you write it.

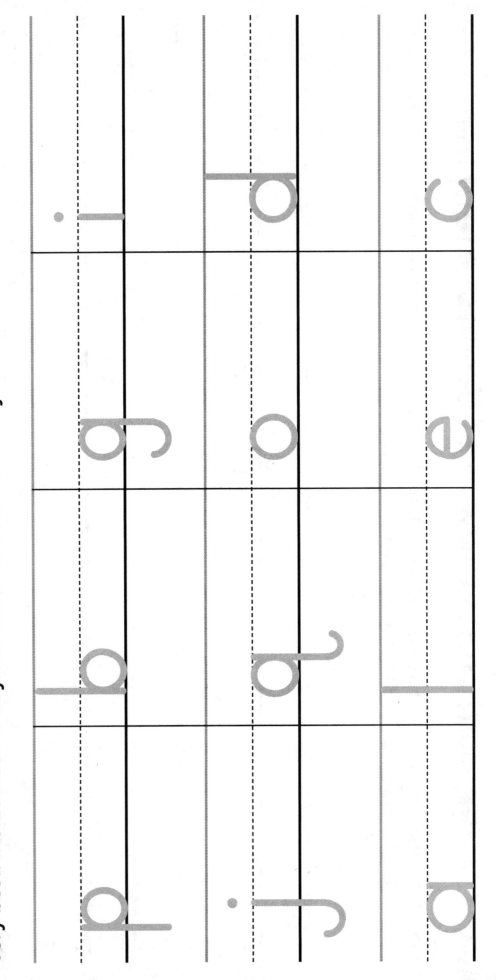

p	b	g	i
j	q	o	d
a	l	e	c

Cumulative Review and Assessment *(cont.)*

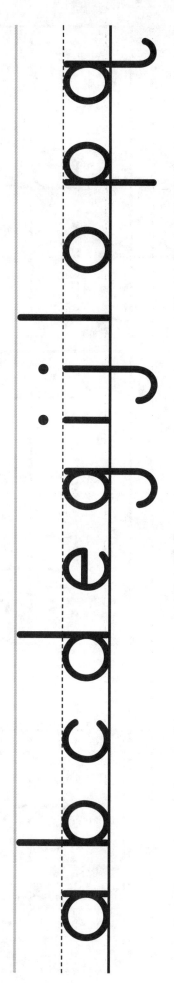

a b c d e g i j l o p q

Look how many letters you already know!

Now go back over the letters you have written on pages 125 and 126. Find the letters that you think are your very best and use a crayon to draw a circle around those letters. Show your circled letters to your teacher.

Do any of your letters need some extra practice? If you think that you would like to practice any of the letters you know a little more, you may use copies of the Ghost Paper (pages 260–264, 266, 269, 271, 274–276.) When you are proud of all your letters, you will be ready to go on to the next part of the review.

Cumulative Review and Assessment *(cont.)*

Tani has written her best letters here, and she has left space for you to write yours.

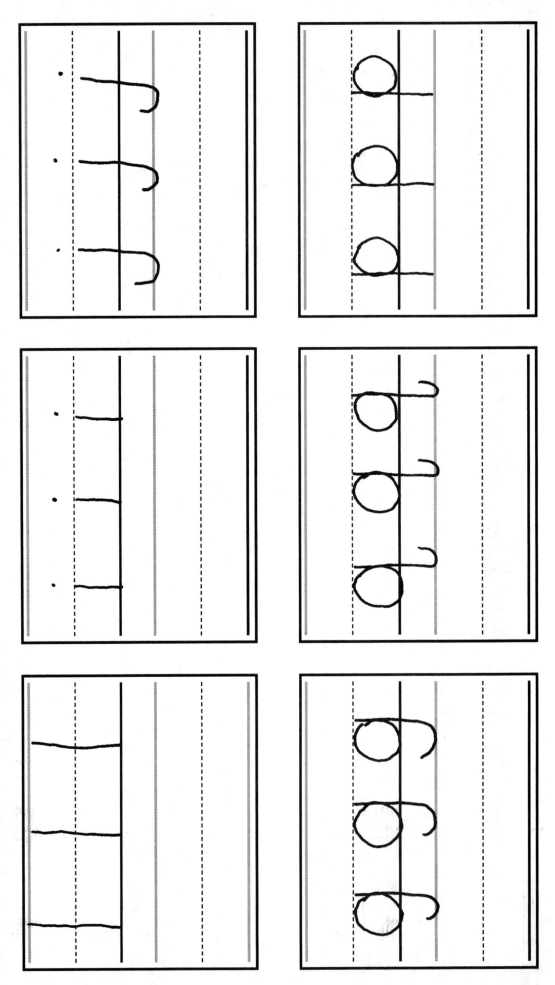

l l l

i i i

j j j

g g g

q q q

p p p

Cumulative Review and Assessment *(cont.)*

Here are some more of Tani's letters. Write your letters under Tani's letters.

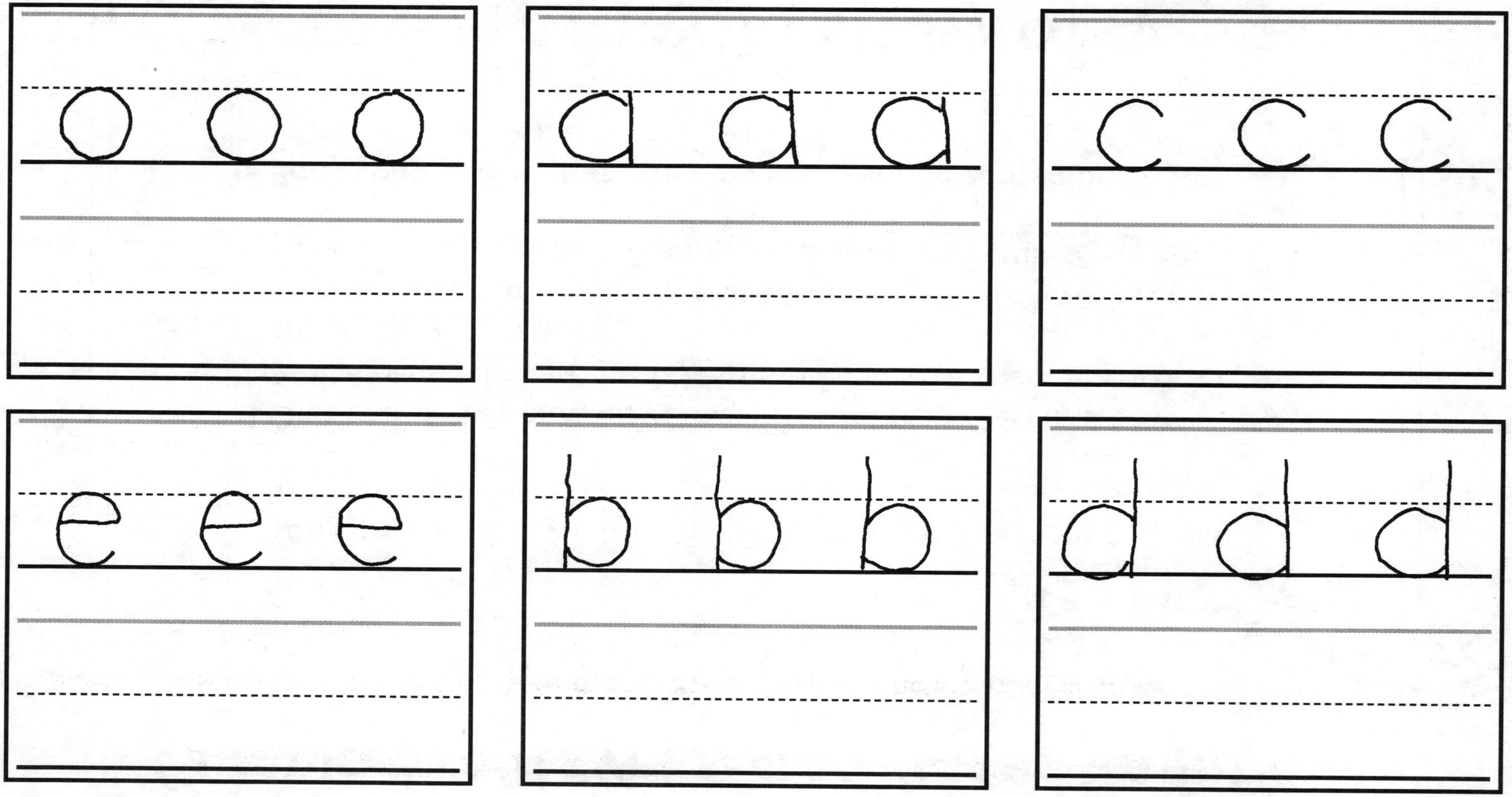

How do your letters look?

Cumulative Review and Assessment *(cont.)*

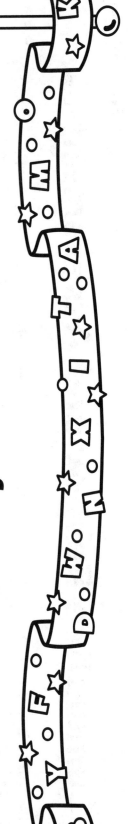

You know so many letters now that we can use them to make lots and lots of words.

On the next two pages, you will find many different words. Ask your teacher to read them to you. Next to each word is a space for you to write the word all by yourself. You know how to write letters that are used to make these words, so it will be easy if you take your time and are careful!

Each song you have learned will help you to remember how to make each of the letters. Are you ready?

Get ready to show off!

Cumulative Review and Assessment *(cont.)*

Write these words.

lid bid

pod bag

pig gap

gob job

Cumulative Review and Assessment *(cont.)*

Write these words.

doll	able
peg	pie
cap	dip
jab	dog

Section 3

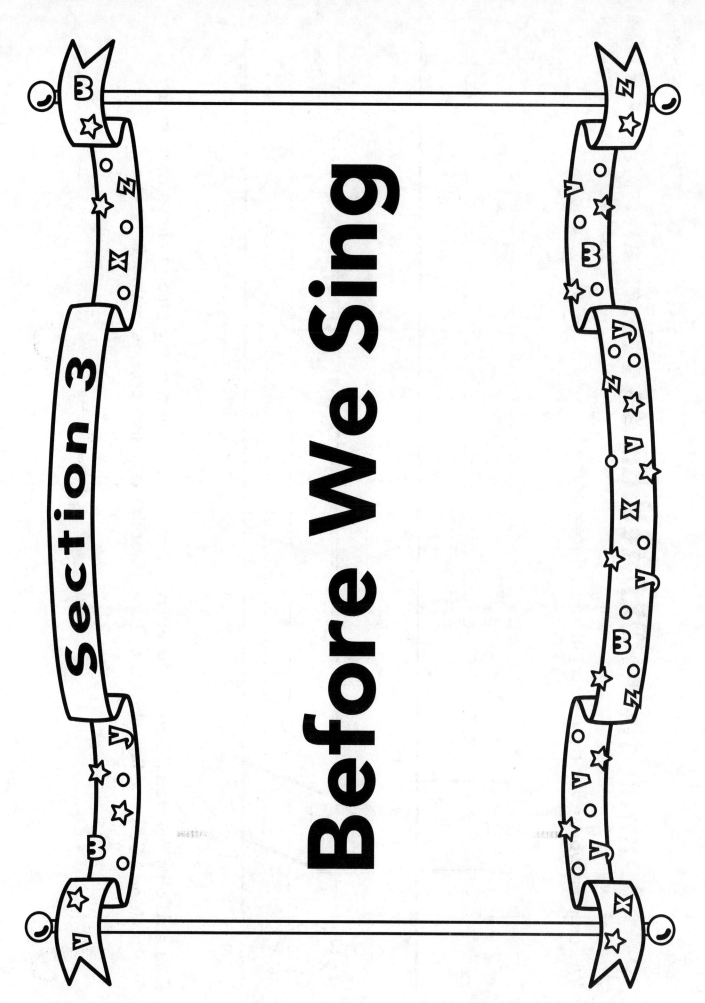

Before We Sing

Slanted Lines

You can already make nice, straight lines. Make some here.

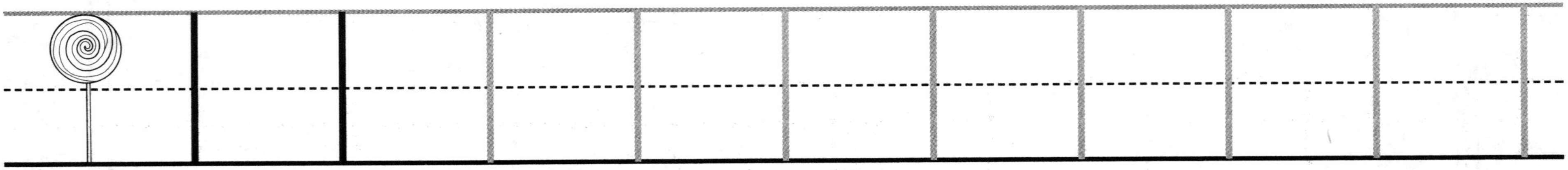

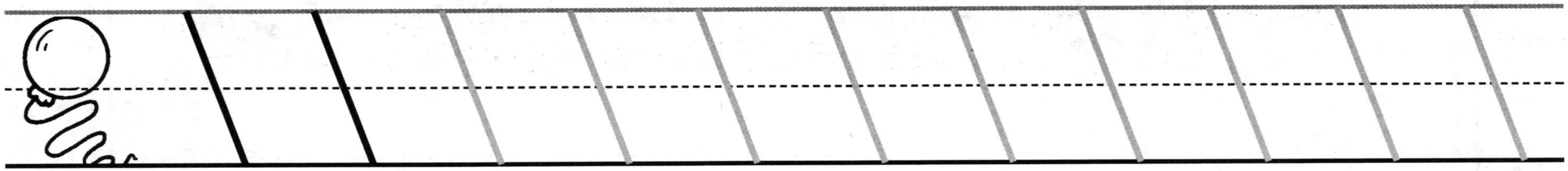

The straight lines you made by the lollipop are not the same as the straight lines that are by the balloon. Can you tell what is different about these two groups of lines?

Slanted Lines *(cont.)*

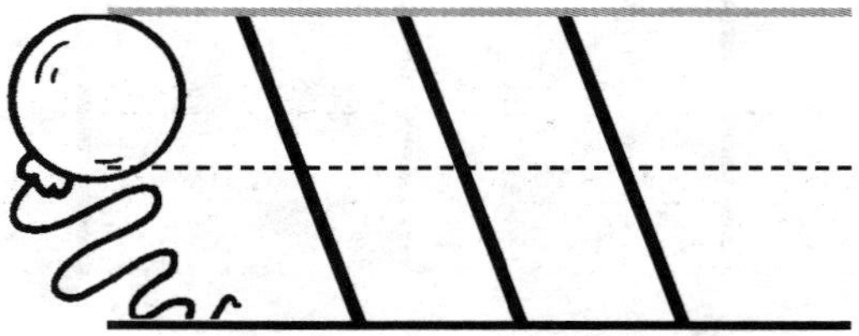

The lines by the balloon are slanted.
A slanted line is a straight line that seems to be falling. It can fall this way. \

Or it can fall this way. /

Let's make some slanted lines between two other lines. To make the slanted line, start at the top of one line and go to the bottom of the next.

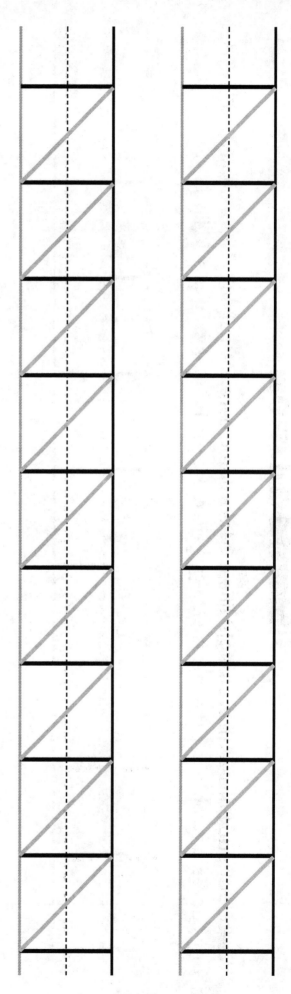

Slanted Lines *(cont.)*

We'll do some more of those **slanted** lines here. Are the lines straight? There should not be any curves or wobbles. The line is straight even though it looks as if it is falling.

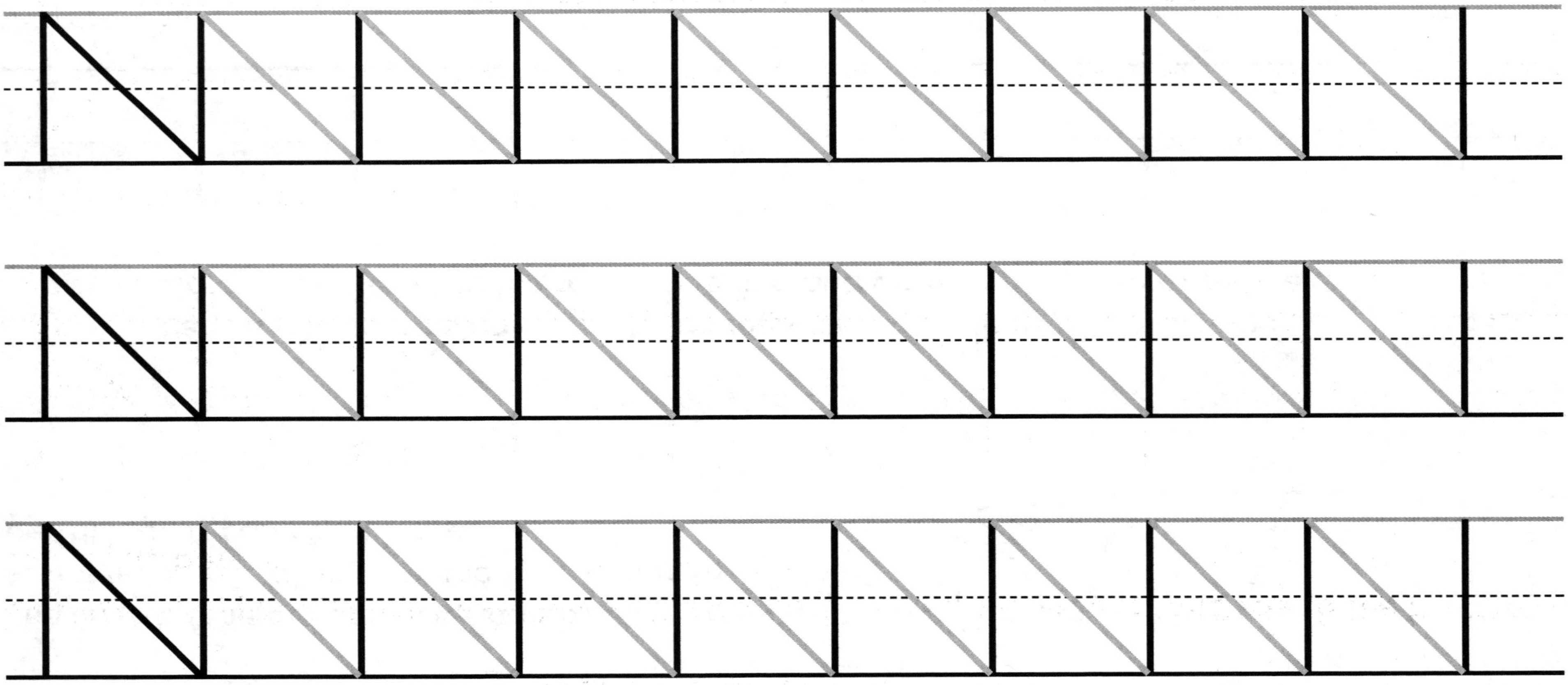

Slanted Lines *(cont.)*

Now let's try slanting lines the other way! This time go from the top of one line to the bottom of the line before.

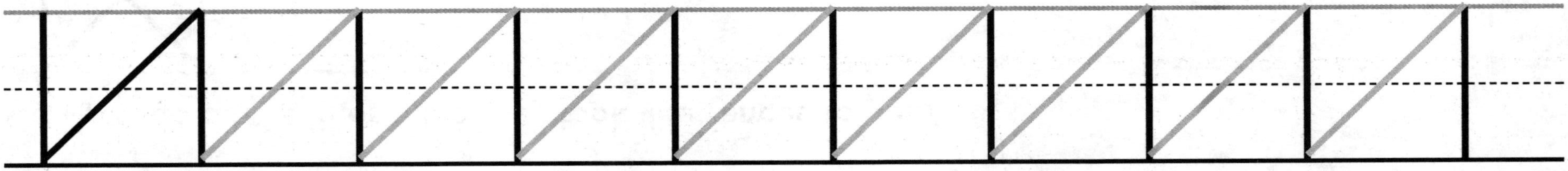

Can you slant both ways?

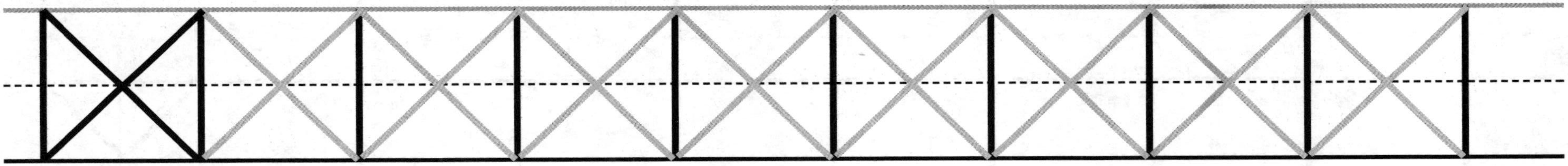

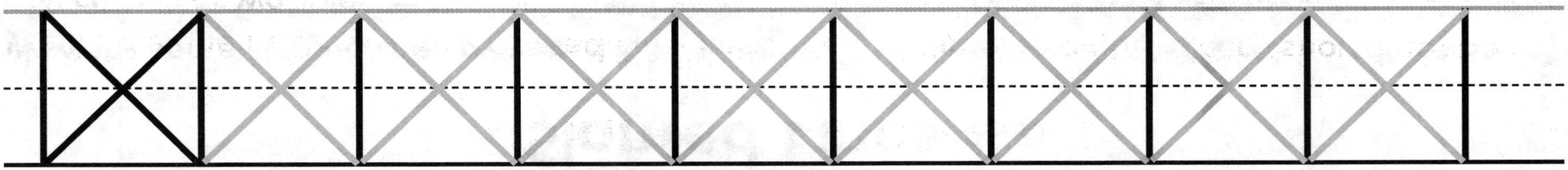

Slanted Lines *(cont.)*

Now try some slanted lines by yourself.

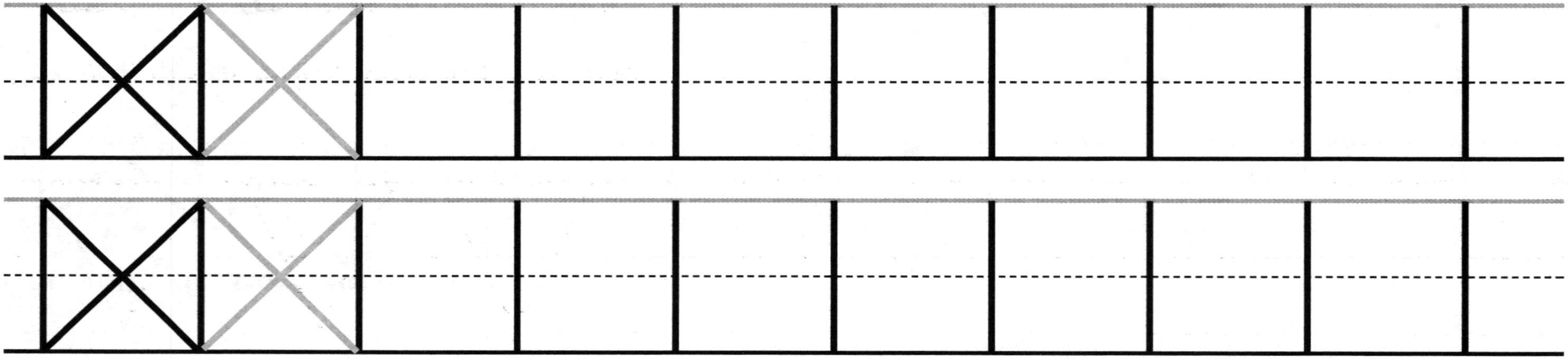

Can you do all the lines? Do they look like fences to you?

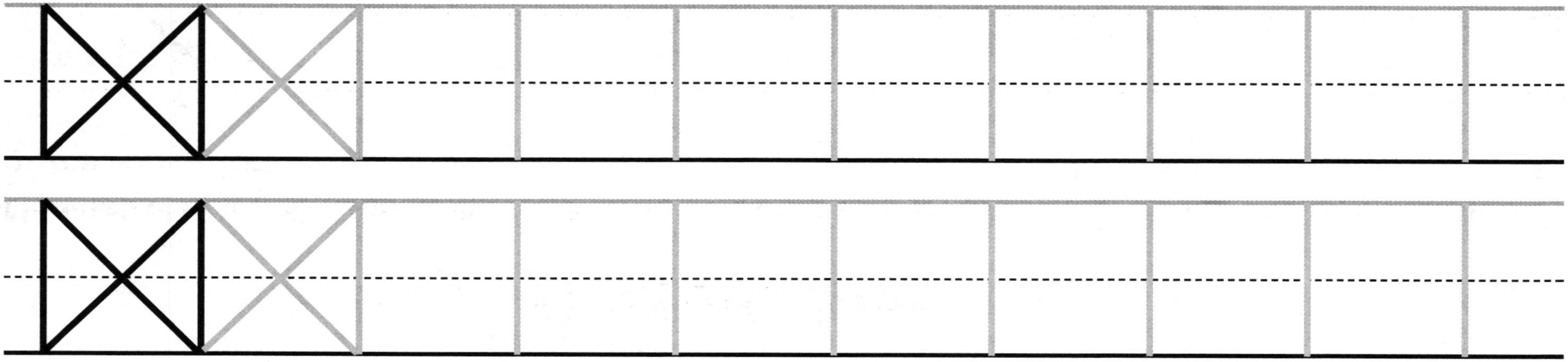

Slanted Lines *(cont.)*

Can you make a chair with straight lines?

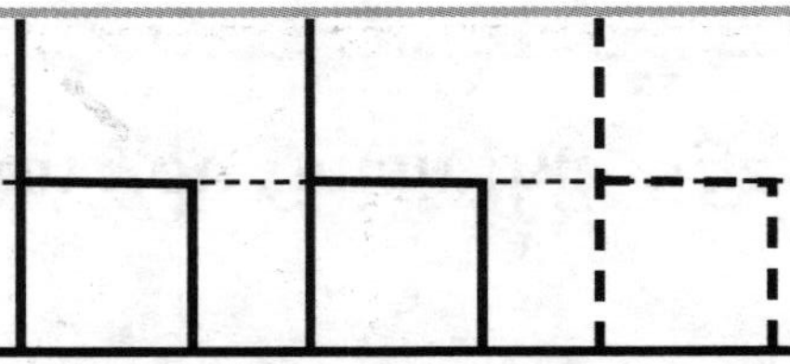

Can you make a tent with straight lines?

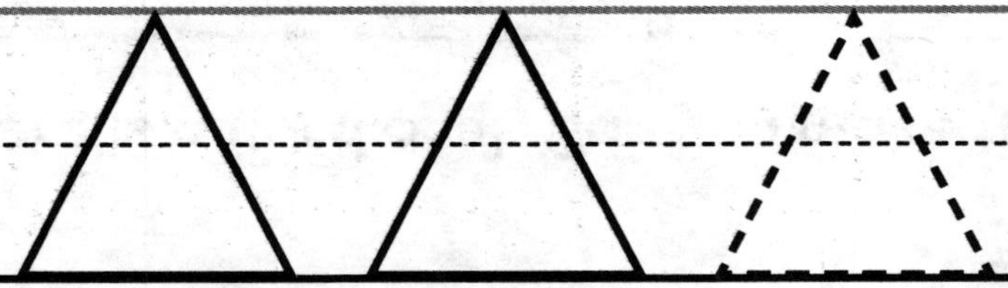

Can you make a box with straight lines?

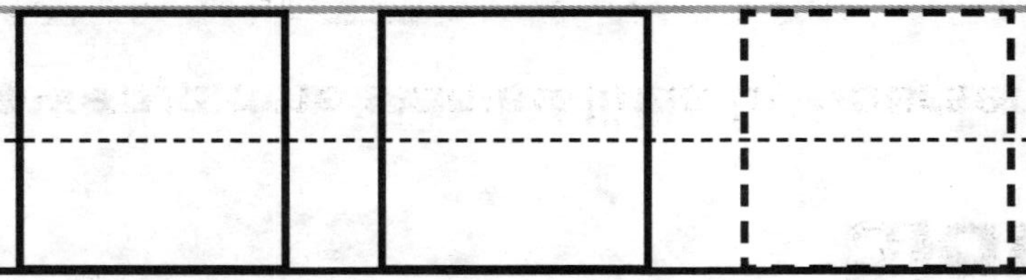

Slanted Lines *(cont.)*

These slanted lines look like a kite. Draw some kites.

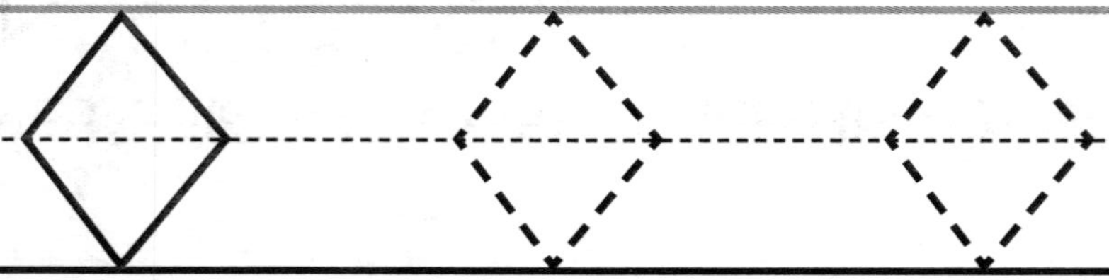

Here is a hard one! Can you make this shape?

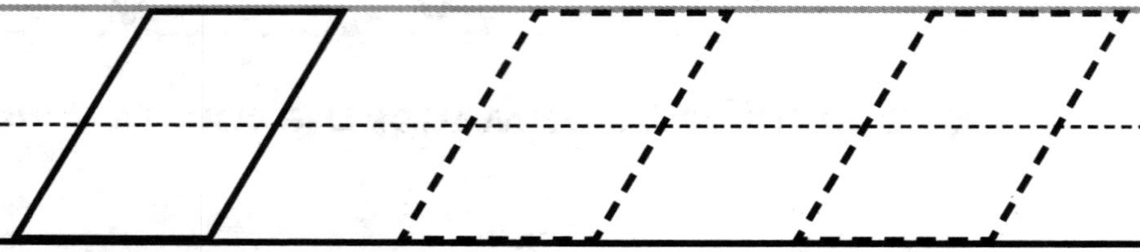

Can you finish this zigzag?

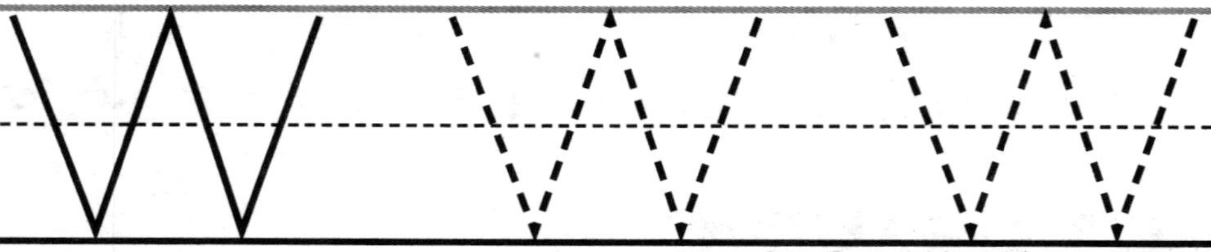

Slanted Lines *(cont.)*

This box is long and skinny. Draw some more boxes.

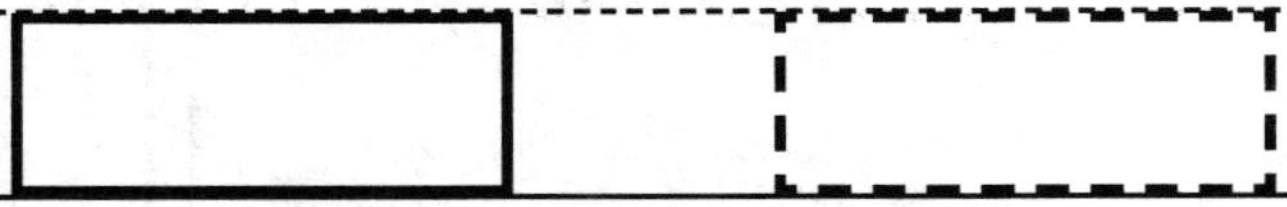

Does this shape look like a flower? Draw some more flowers.

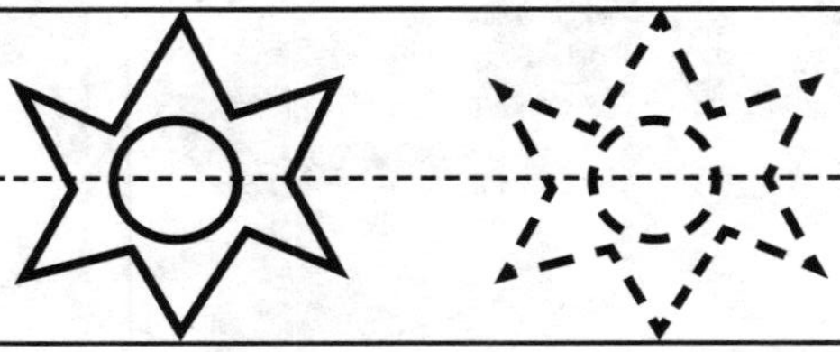

An arrow tells you which way to go!  Draw some more arrows.

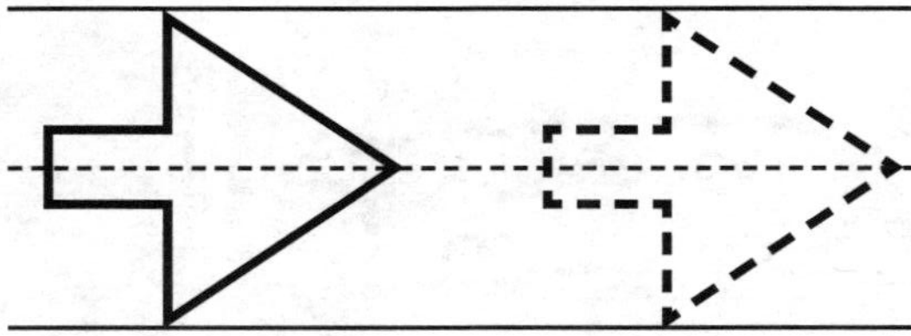

Section 3

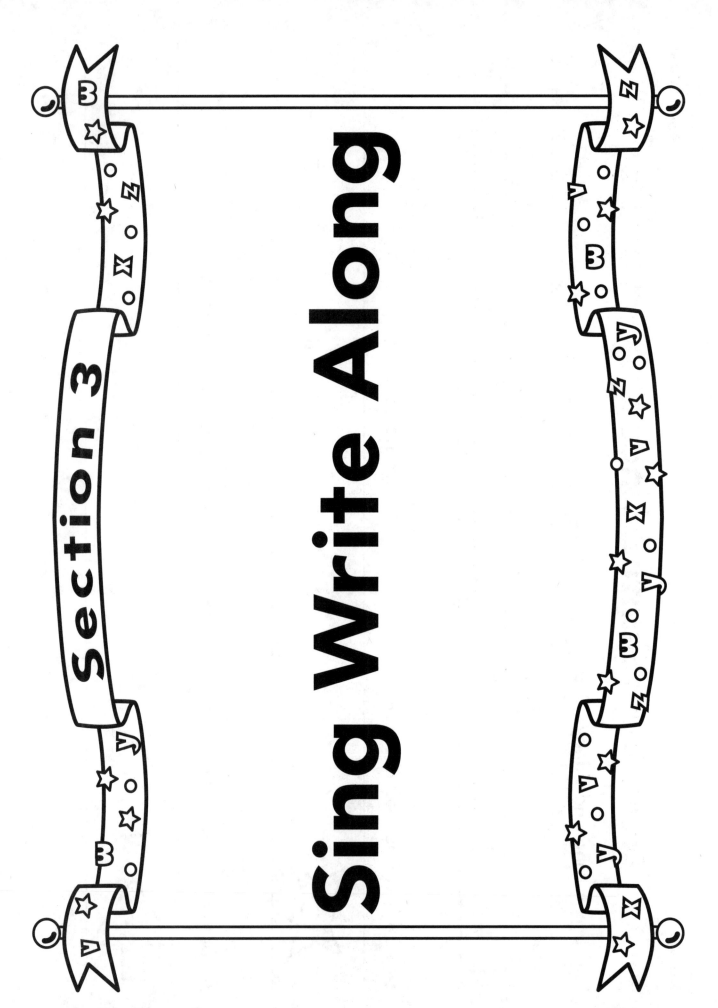

Sing Write Along

Teaching the Letters v, w, y, x, and z

Write Rhymes Poster for the Letters **w, v, x, y,** and **z**

v x w y z

w, v, and x, y, z —
All these letters are great ones;
Although we know they cross or slant
Their lines are always straight ones.

w x y z v

Teaching the Letters v, w, y, x, and z *(cont.)*

This creature looks like an owl.
Her name is Vicky. Do you see
the slanted lines that are on her face?

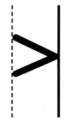

v

Look at the lines that make the letter **v**. You can write the letter **v** by putting together two of the slanted lines that we have practiced. You will begin on the dotted middle guide line. The first slant goes this way \ .Then the second goes the other way /, like this. The two slanted lines meet at the bottom and that makes the letter **v**.

v v v v v v v v v v v

Teaching the Letters v, w, y, x, and z *(cont.)*

Here is a place for you to practice writing the letter **v**. Be sure the point of the letter **v** is right on the dark bottom guide line, not under it.

Don't let the letter **v** be fat, like this!

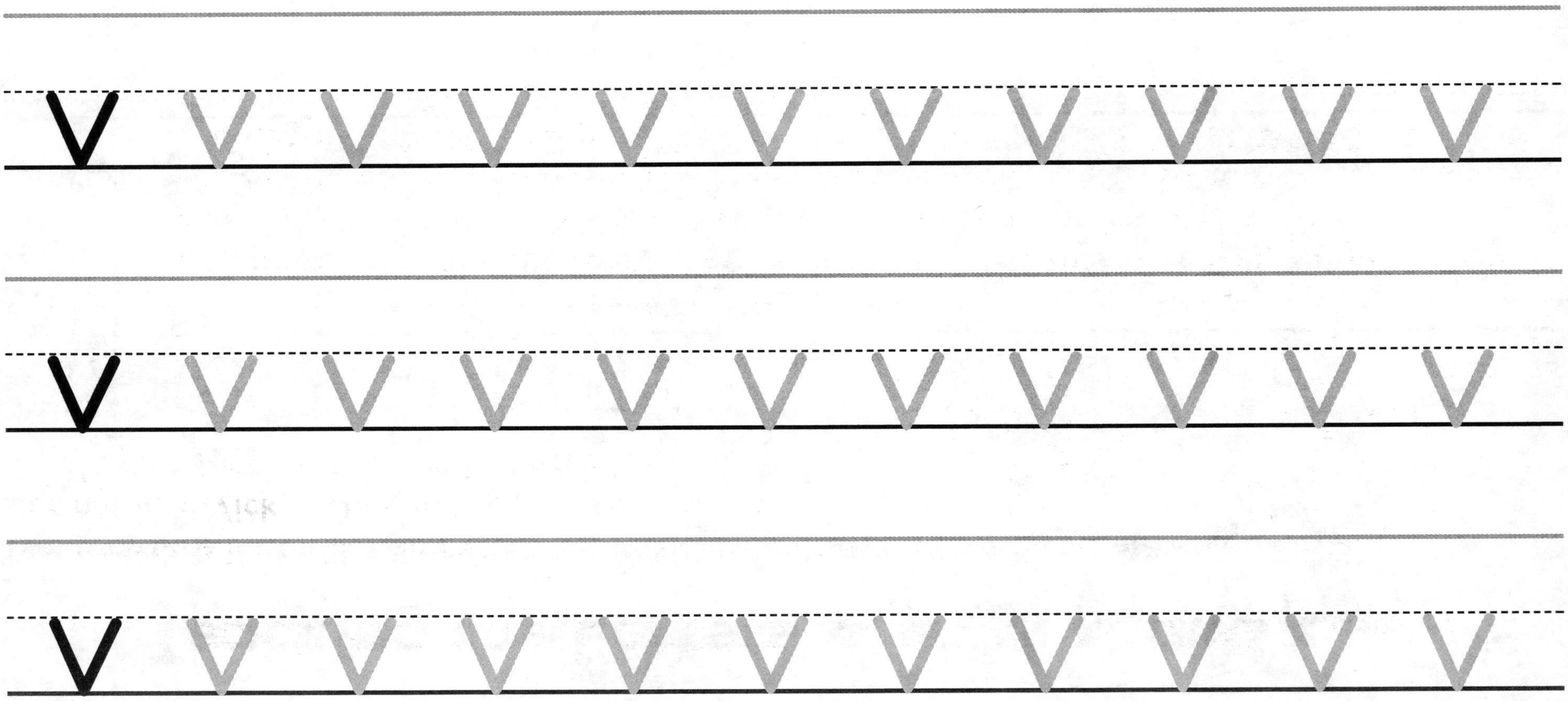

Teaching the Letters v, w, y, x, and z *(cont.)*

Now try writing the letter **v** all by yourself! Say the name of the letter as you write it.

v v

v v

v v

v v

Teaching the Letters v, w, y, x, and z *(cont.)*

This is wonderful Willa! Her letter, **w**, is easy now that you can write the letter **v**. The letter **w** is just a second **v** attached to the first one!

w

If your **w** looks like this, *w* then your lines are too slanted. The slanted lines that make the letter **w** are almost straight up and down, but not quite.

Which **w** has slanted lines that are just right?

w w w w w w w w

w w w w w w w w

Teaching the Letters v, w, y, x, and z *(cont.)*

After you have finished writing one v, put the second one so close that they touch and you will have the letter w.

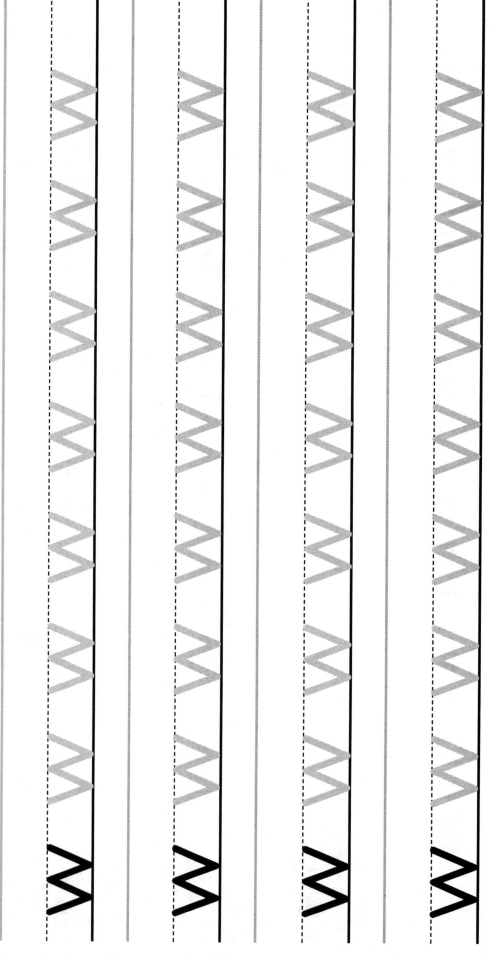

w w w w w w w w

w w w w w w w w

w w w w w w w w

w w w w w w w w

Teaching the Letters v, w, y, x, and z *(cont.)*

Now try writing Willa's letter, w, all by yourself. Say the name of the letter as you write it.

w w

w w

w w

w w

Teaching the Letters v, w, y, x, and z *(cont.)*

Now let's mix up the two new letters, **v** and **w**. Remember to say the name of each letter as you write it.

v v

v w v w

w v w v

w w

Teaching the Letters v, w, y, x, and z *(cont.)*

Yellowbird has a letter that looks a lot like the letter **v**. But Yellowbird's tail hangs down under the dark bottom guide line, just like the tail on Gus, the cat; Queek, the monkey; and Percival, the possum.

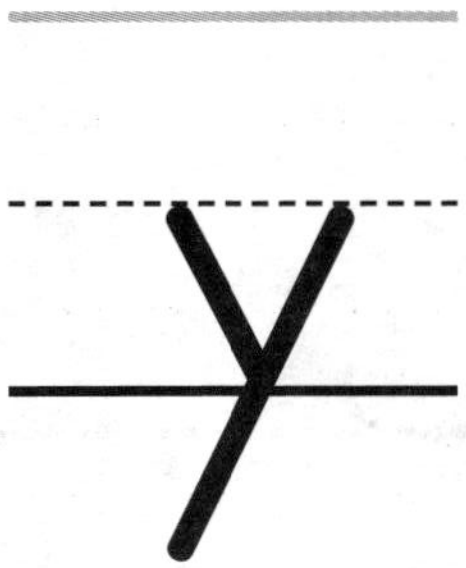

This new letter is the letter y. It looks like the letter **v** with a tail. To write the letter y begin with the letter **v**. But when you make the second line, keep on going under the dark bottom guide line to make a tail for Yellowbird!

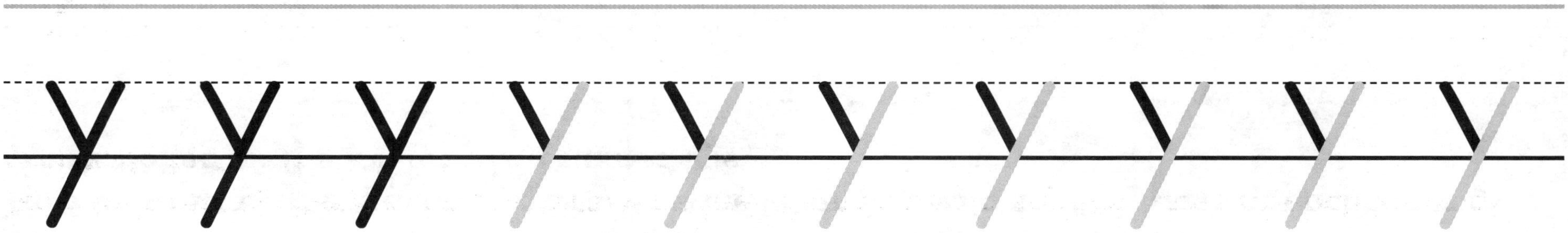

Teaching the Letters v, w, y, x, and z *(cont.)*

Yellowbird's tail does not have a hook like the letters g and q have. It does not hang straight like the letter p. The tail for y is a slanted line.

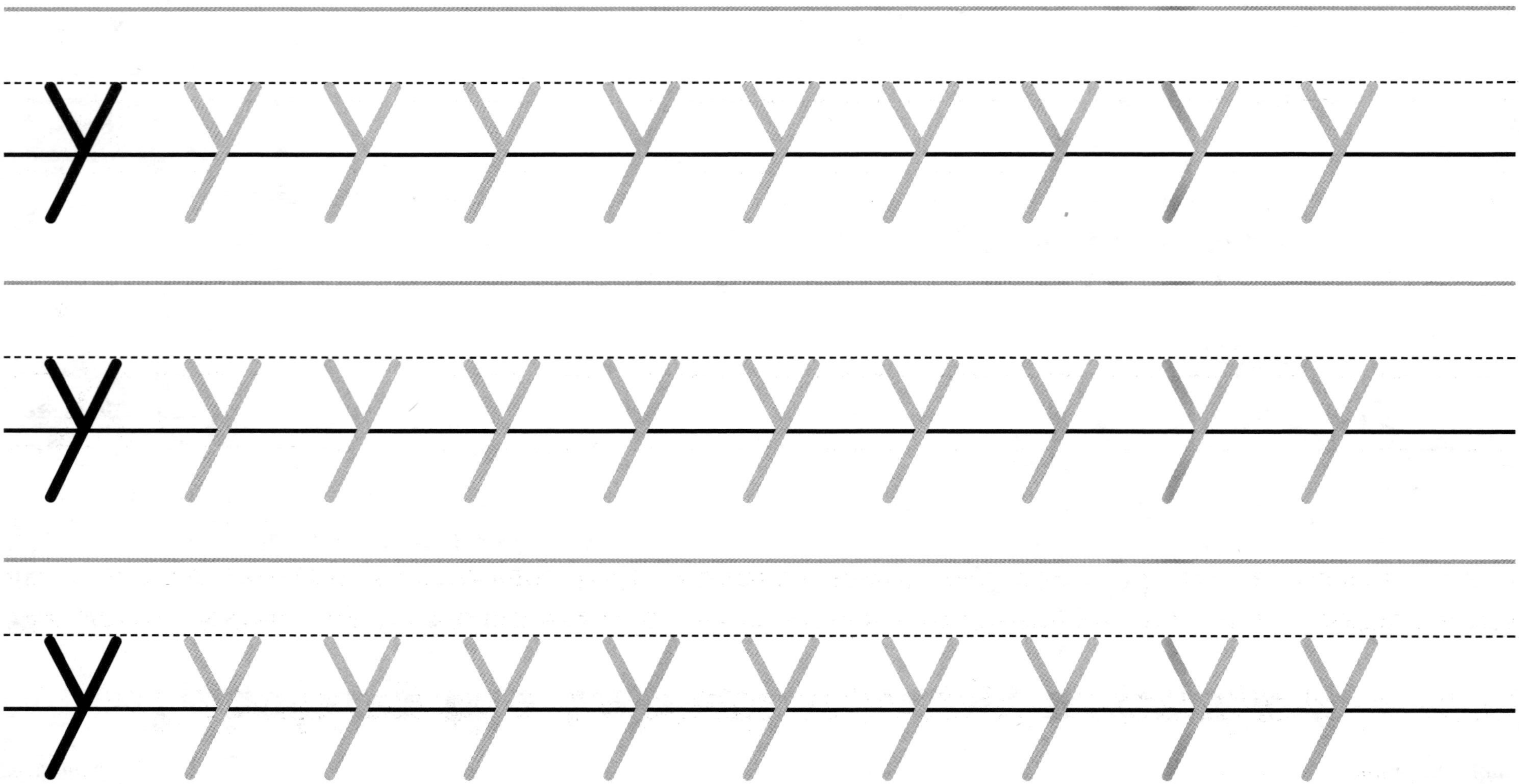

Teaching the Letters v, w, y, x, and z *(cont.)*

The letter v is made up of two slanted lines. When you make the tail for the letter y, you will keep the same slant as your second line. Try some here. Say the name of the letter as you write it.

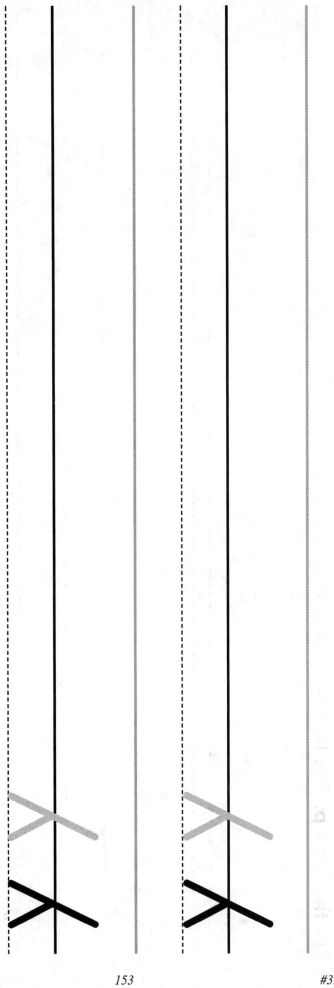

y y

y y

y y

Teaching the Letters v, w, y, x, and z *(cont.)*

Let's try all three of these new letters (**v**, **w**, and y) that use slanted lines. Be sure to say the name of each letter as you write it.

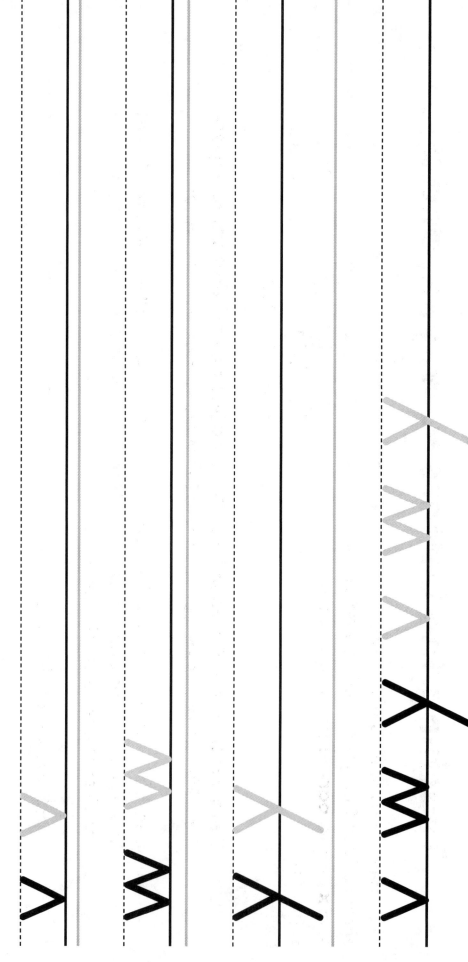

v v

w w

y y

v w y v w y

Teaching the Letters v, w, y, x, and z *(cont.)*

This new letter, **x**, is made of two slanted lines that cross in the middle. The **x** makes part of the wings of the butterfly.

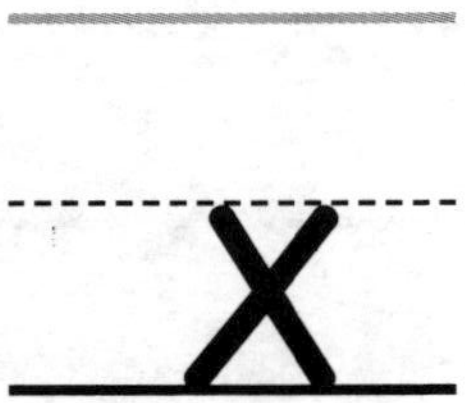

The **x** sits between the dotted middle guide line and the dark bottom guide line. The letter **x** does not have a tail that hangs down in the water.

Begin by making a slanted line, like this. \ Then make a second slanted line that goes the other way. / Make sure your second line crosses over the first one to write the letter **x**.

Finish writing the letter **x**.

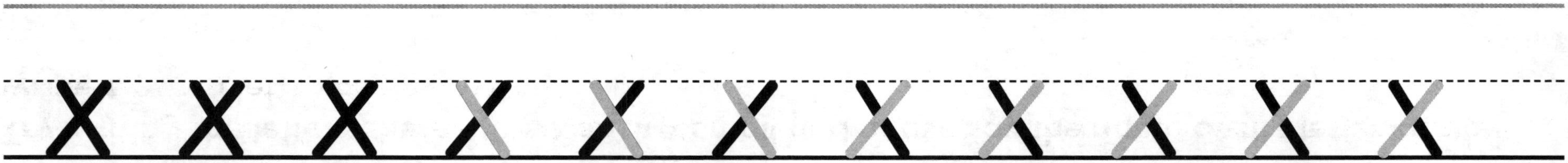

Teaching the Letters v, w, y, x, and z *(cont.)*

Try writing the letter **x** here. Keep each **x** small and neat. Say the name of the letter as you write it.

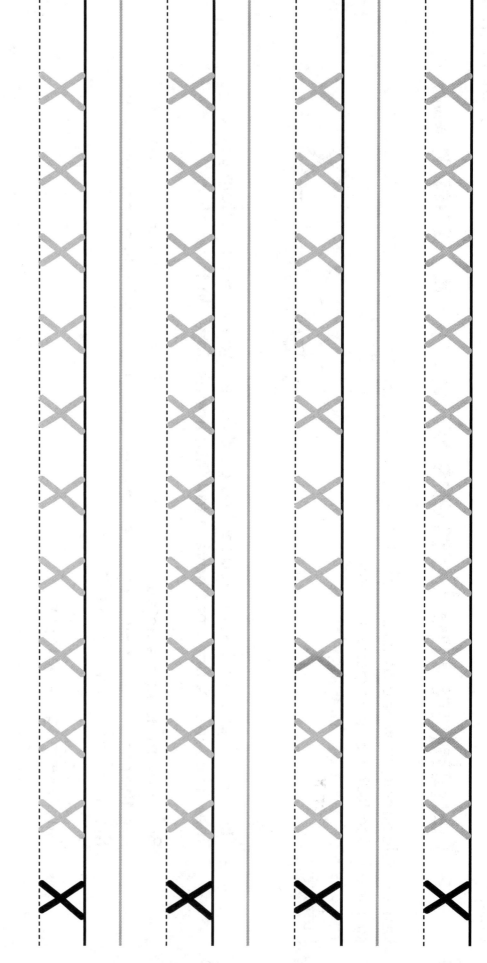

x x x x x x x x x x x

x x x x x x x x x x x

x x x x x x x x x x x

x x x x x x x x x x x

Teaching the Letters v, w, y, x, and z *(cont.)*

Do not slant your lines too much, or the letter **x** will not be the right size. It will look like this x. The letter **x** cannot be too wide!

Write the letter **x**. Say the name of the letter as you write it.

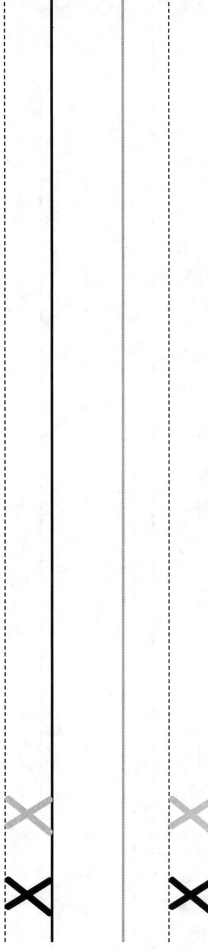

x x

x x

x x

Teaching the Letters v, w, y, x, and z *(cont.)*

We will add the letter **x** to the other letters (**v**, **w**, and y) with slanted lines. Write the letters with slanted lines. Say the name of each letter as you write it.

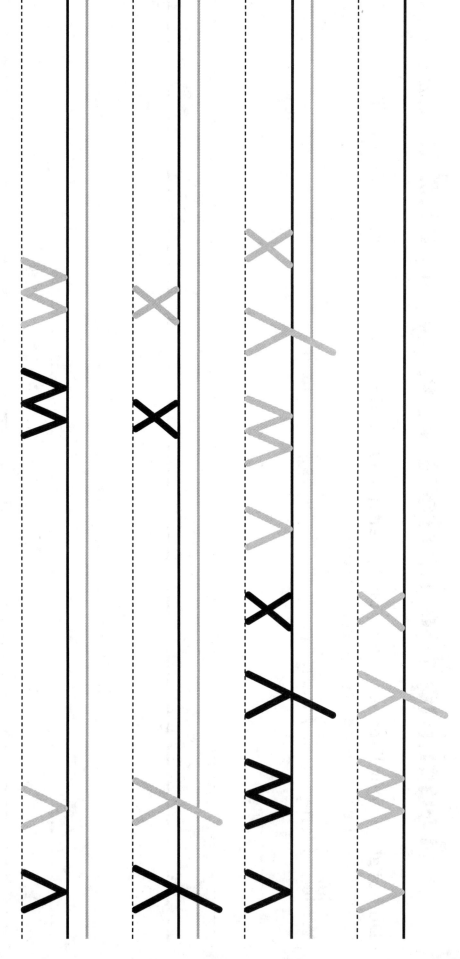

v v w w

y y x x

v w y x v w y x

v w y x

Teaching the Letters v, w, y, x, and z *(cont.)*

Here is the last of our slanted letters. It is the great dragon, Zilch! His letter is the letter **z**.

z

Can you see something very different about the letter **z**? Two of the straight lines go sideways. One follows along the dotted middle guide line, and one follows the dark bottom guide line.

To write the letter **z**, start with the line that goes sideways along the dotted middle guide line. Then make the slanted line. Finally, make the line that goes sideways along the dark bottom guide line.

z z z z z z z z z z z

Teaching the Letters v, w, y, x, and z *(cont.)*

Try writing the letter **z** here. Follow the arrows to make it correctly. Say the name of the letter as you write it.

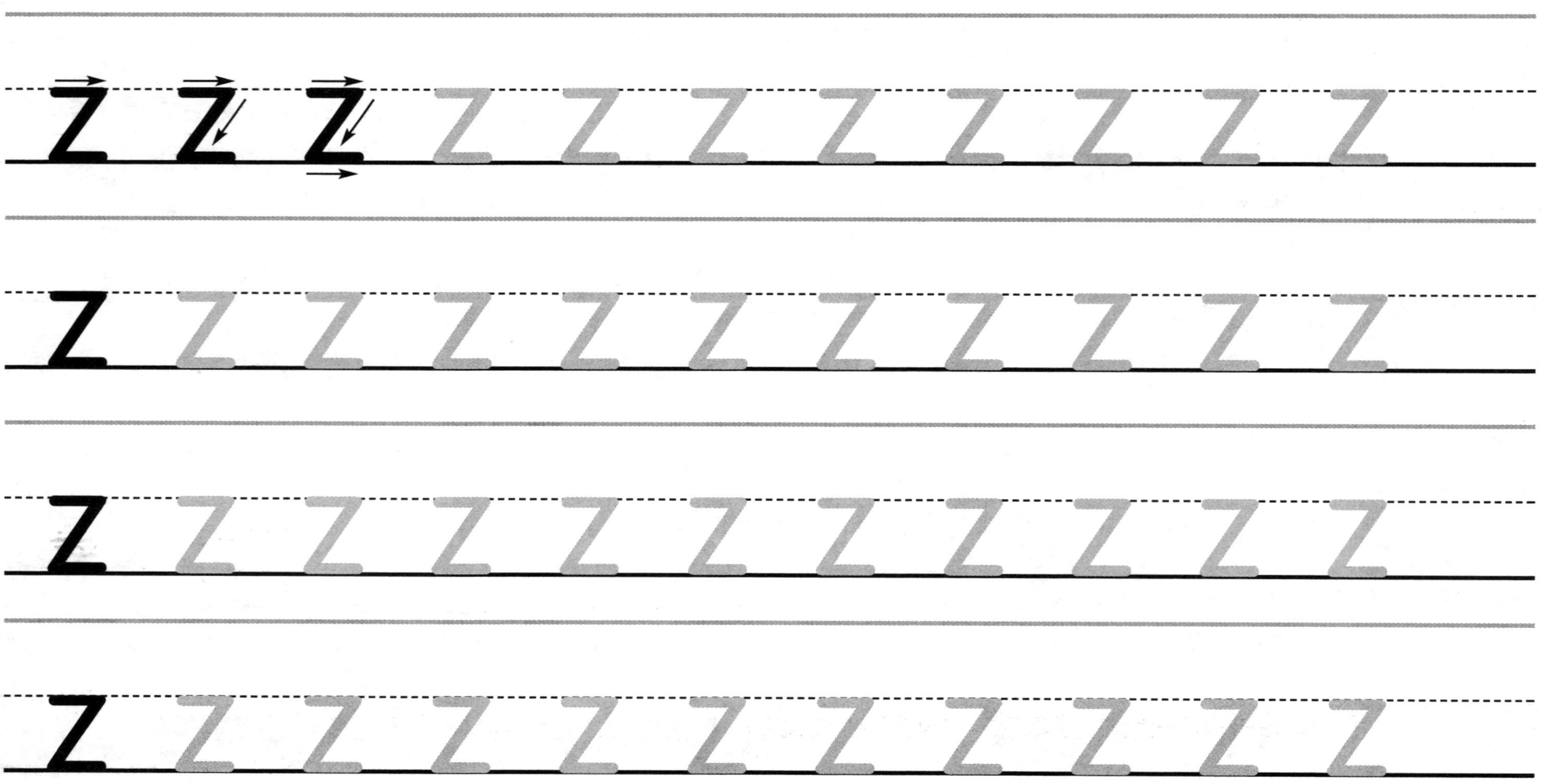

Teaching the Letters v, w, y, x, and z *(cont.)*

Now you can practice writing the letter z by yourself. Be neat and careful as you write. Say the name of the letter as you write it.

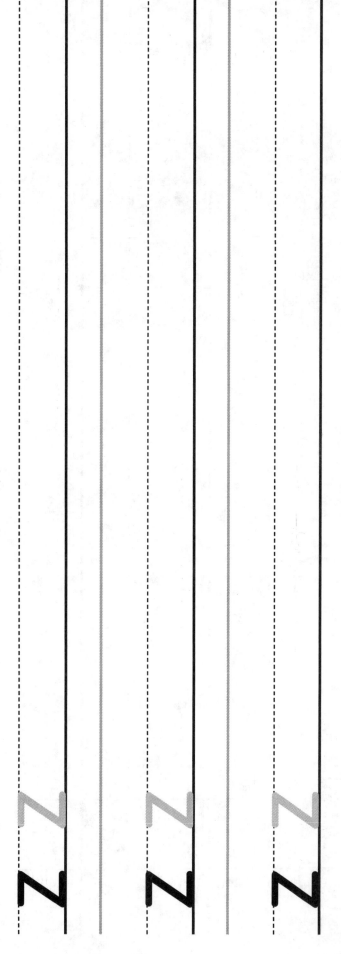

z z

z z

z z

z z

Teaching the Letters v, w, y, x, and z *(cont.)*

Now let's write all our letters (**v**, **w**, **x**, y, and **z**) that have slanted lines. Say the name of each letter as you write it.

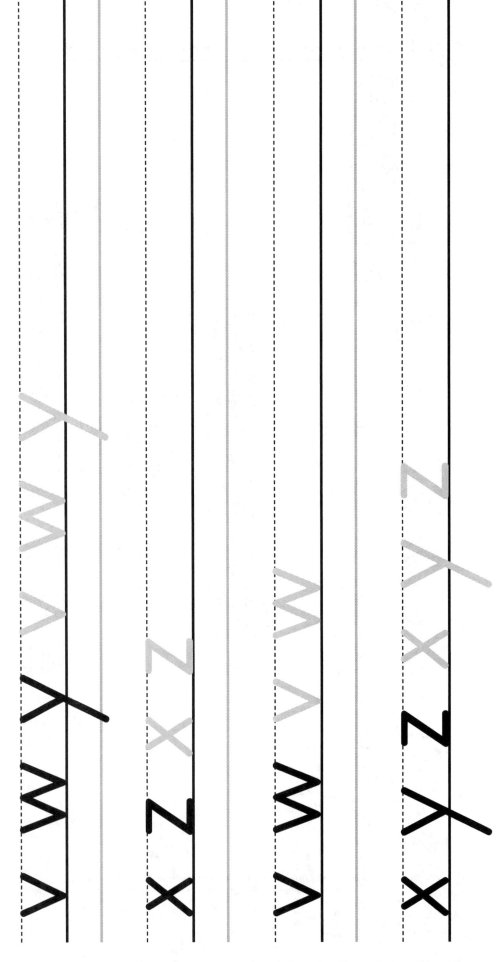

v w y v w y

x z x z

v w v w

x y z x y z

Section 3

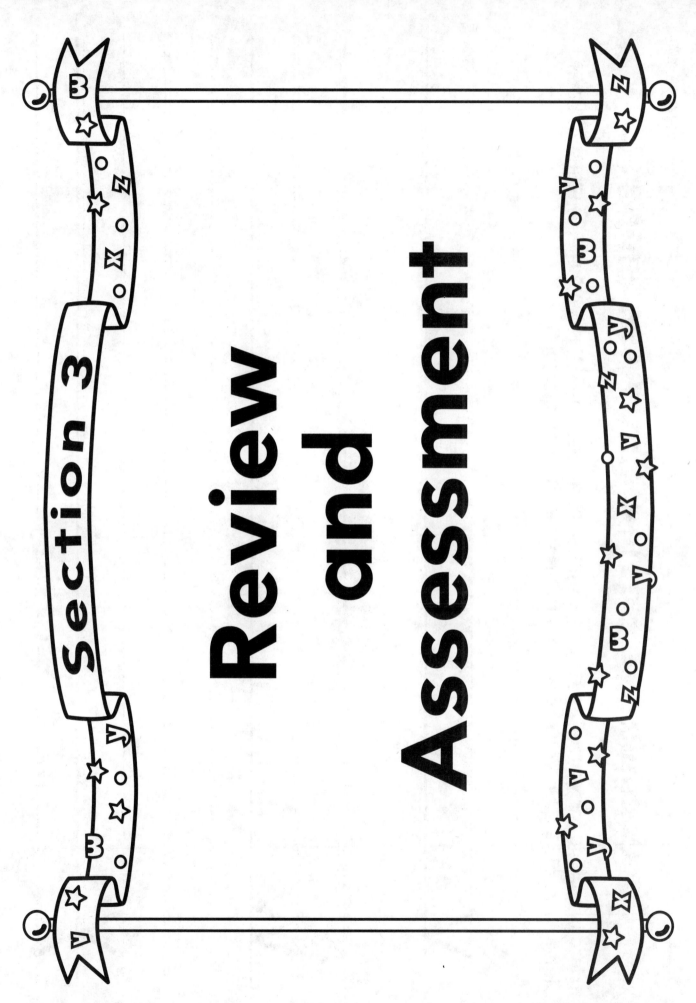

Review and Assessment

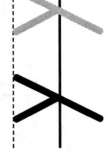

Cumulative Review and Assessment

Here is a place for you to practice writing the letters **v**, **w**, and y. Do you see ways that these letters are alike? Do you see ways that these letters are different?

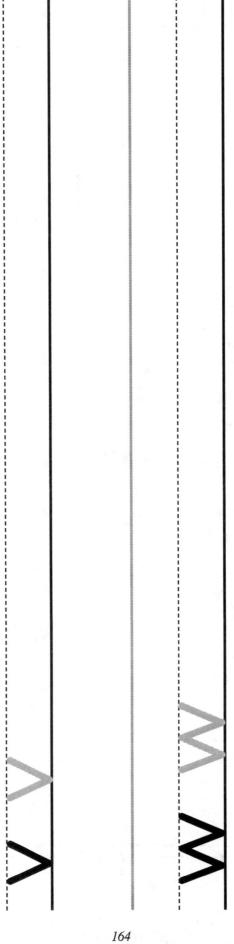

v v

w w

y y

Cumulative Review and Assessment *(cont.)*

Now practice writing the newest letters that you have learned. Those letters are x and z. Say the name of each letter as you write it.

x x

z z

x x

z z

Cumulative Review and Assessment *(cont.)*

Now let's do all the letters (**v**, **w**, **x**, y, and **z**) that have slanted lines. Say the name of each letter as you write it.

v v w w

x x y y

z z x x

y y z z

Cumulative Review and Assessment *(cont.)*

Here are some letters you already know. Do you remember all of them? Say the name of each letter as you write it.

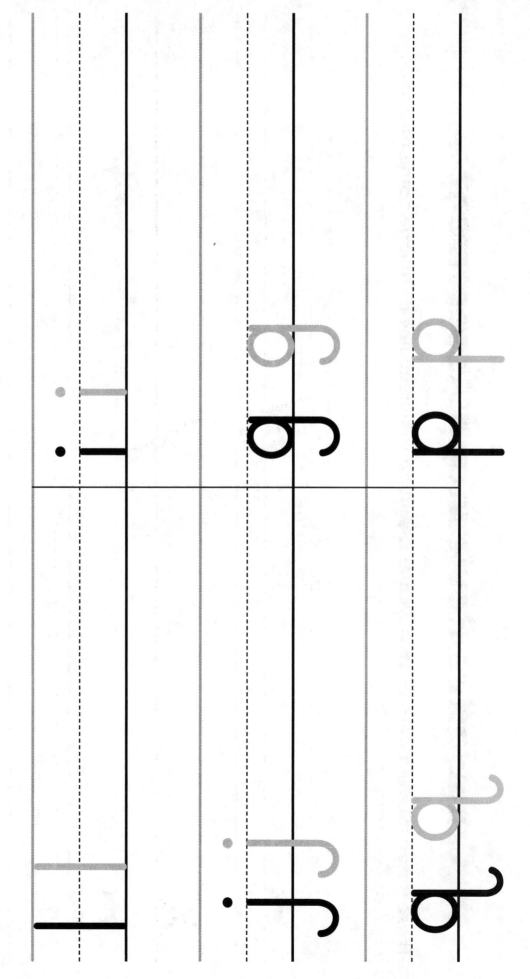

l l

i i

j j

g g

q q

p p

Cumulative Review and Assessment *(cont.)*

These letters are old friends, too. Remember to say the name of each letter as you write it.

o o a a

c c e e

b b d d

Cumulative Review and Assessment *(cont.)*

There are so many letters that you already know! Let's mix them up and see if you can write all of them! Say the name of each letter as you write it.

c	a	o	b
v	x	w	l
d	i	y	e
p	q	g	j

Cumulative Review and Assessment *(cont.)*

Here are more letters that you know. Write them neatly and carefully. Take your time and do not hurry. Say the name of each letter as you write it.

z	d	o	v
i	x	l	a
e	b	q	w
y	g	j	p

Cumulative Review and Assessment *(cont.)*

a b c d e g i j l

o p q v w y x z

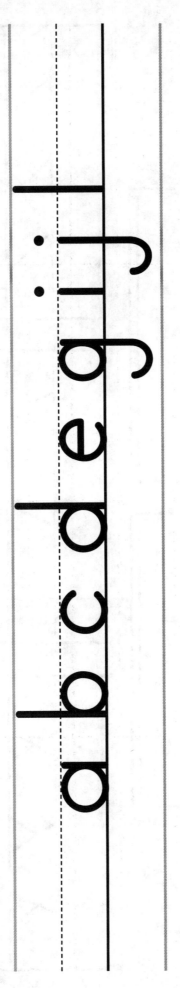

Look at all the letters you know now! Can you say the name of each letter?

Look over pages 169 and 170. Find the letters that you think are your very best, and use a crayon to draw a circle around each of those. Show your best letters to your teacher.

If any of your letters look as if they need more practice, you can always use copies of the Ghost Paper (pages 260–264, 266, 268, 269, 271, 274–276, 281–285). Practice until you are proud of the way your letters look. Then you will be ready to go on.

Cumulative Review and Assessment *(cont.)*

Tani has practiced the letters **v, w, x, y,** and **z.** She has left space for you to practice the same letters.

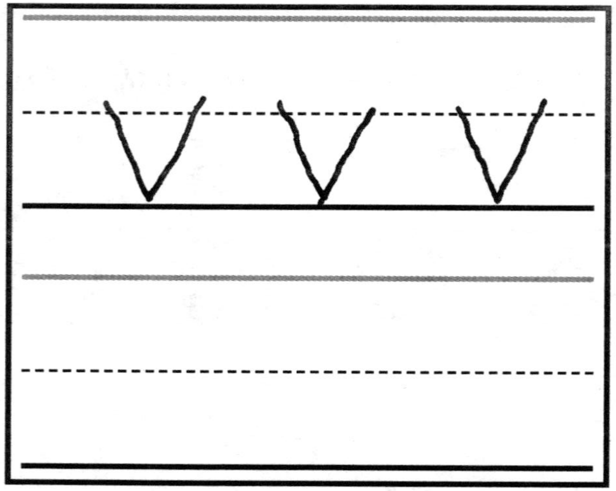

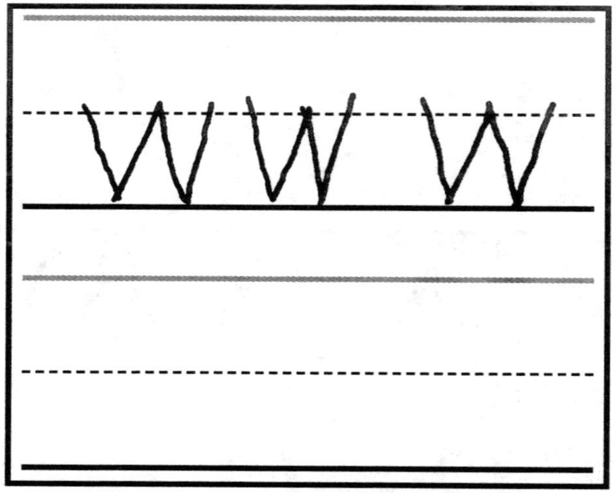

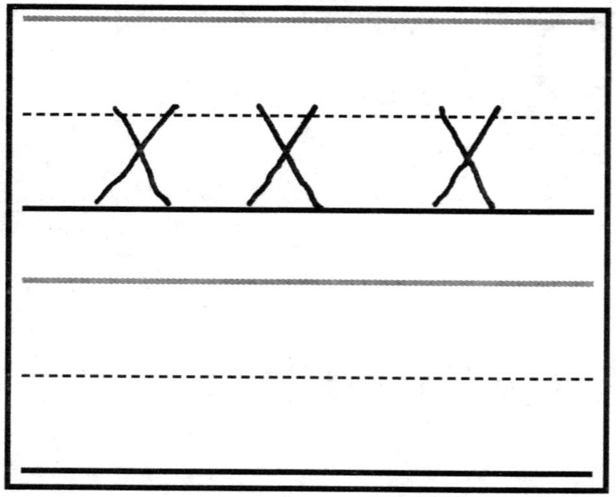

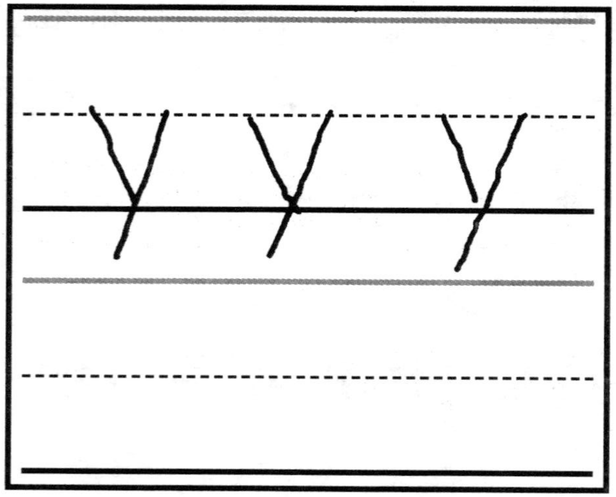

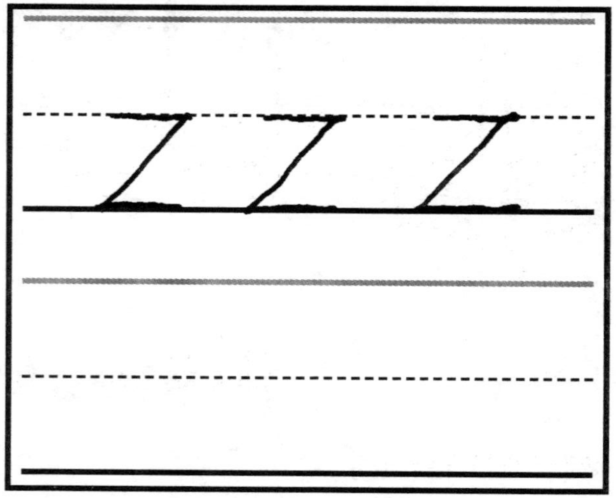

Cumulative Review and Assessment *(cont.)*

Section 4

You have learned so many letters that we can write many, many words.

On the next two pages you will be able to show how well you can write all these letters. Ask your teacher to read the words to you, and then you will write the word by yourself. Take your time and do your very best.

The songs you have learned will help you remember how to write each of these letters.

Get ready to show off!

Cumulative Review and Assessment *(cont.)*

Write these words.

wag	pie
give	zip
bell	big
box	cow

Cumulative Review and Assessment *(cont.)*

Write these words.

dove	bale
joy	pig
zap	way
wave	pail

Section 4

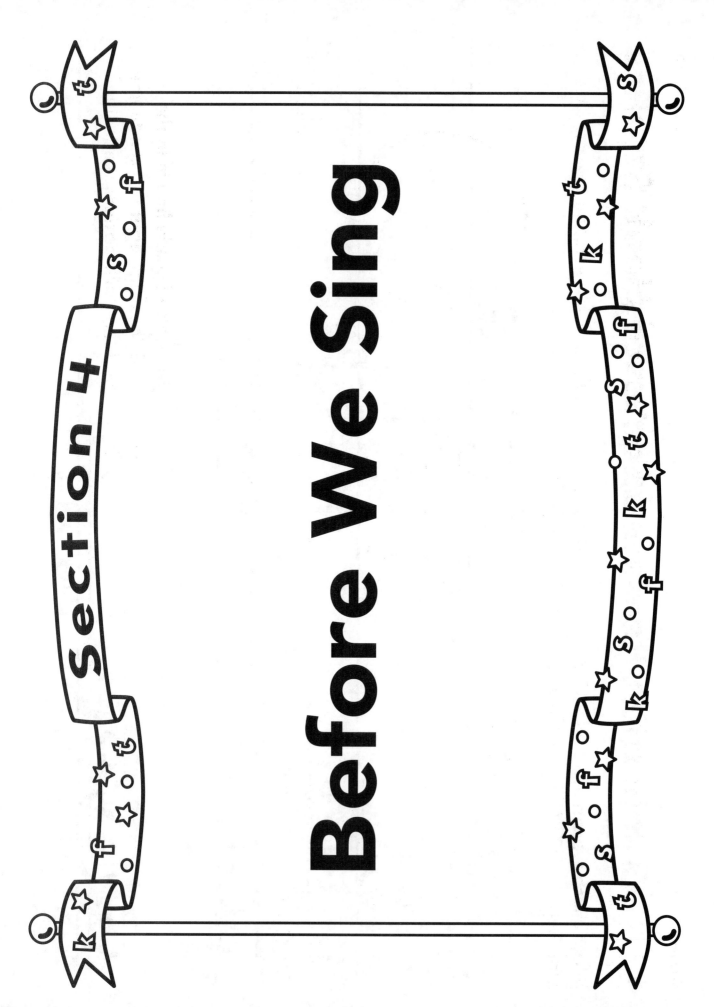

Before We Sing

The Middle of Spaces and Forward Hook Strokes

Do you know the word **middle**? It means in the center, or halfway between two things. This star is in the **middle**, or halfway between the two circles.

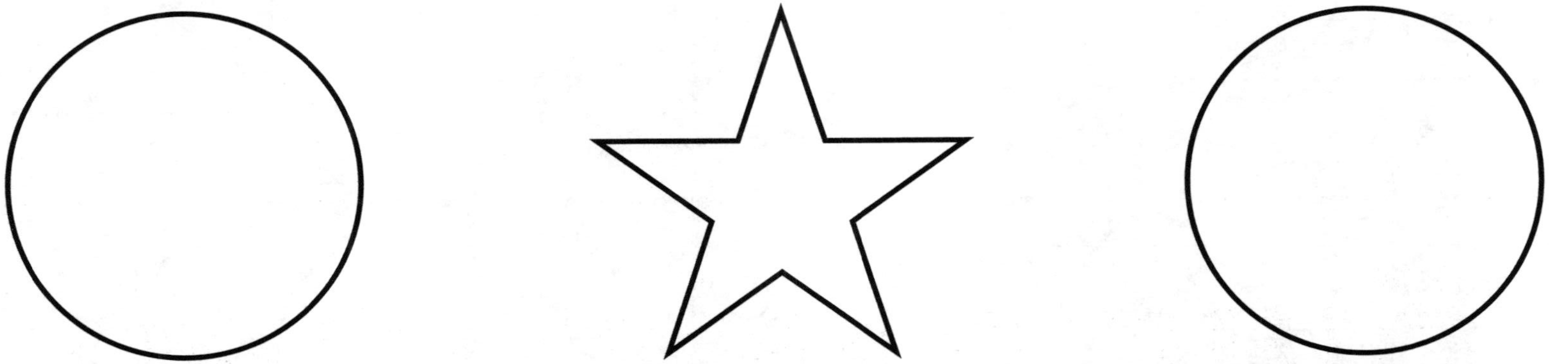

The dot is in the **middle** of the dark bottom guide line.

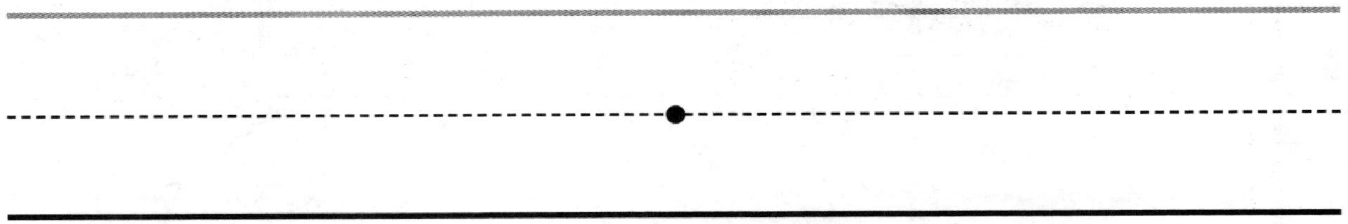

The dotted guide line is in the **middle** of the light top guide line and the dark bottom guide line.

The Middle of Spaces and Forward Hook Strokes *(cont.)*

Here are some circles. Can you put a dot in the middle of each circle? One has been done for you.

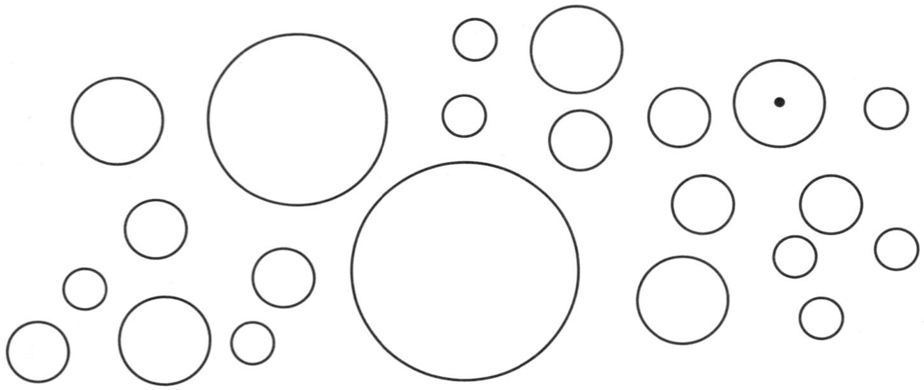

Can you find the middle of each line and put a dot there? One has been done for you.

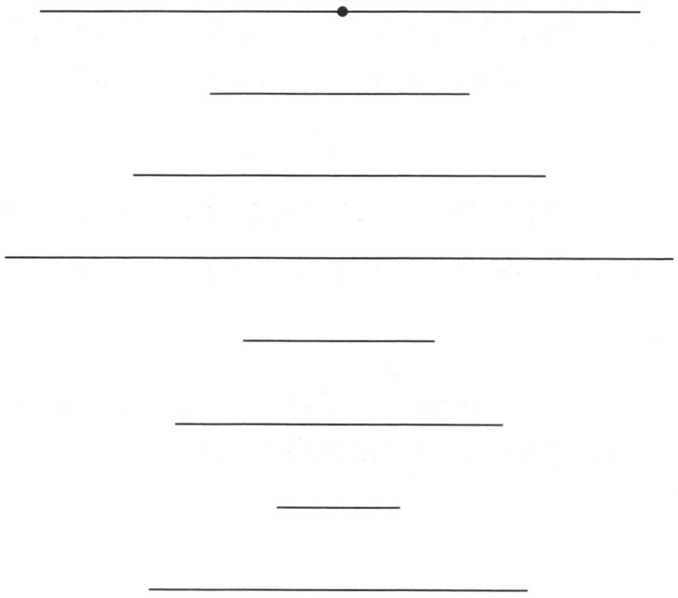

Can you put a little square in the middle of the big square?

The Middle of Spaces and Forward Hook Strokes *(cont.)*

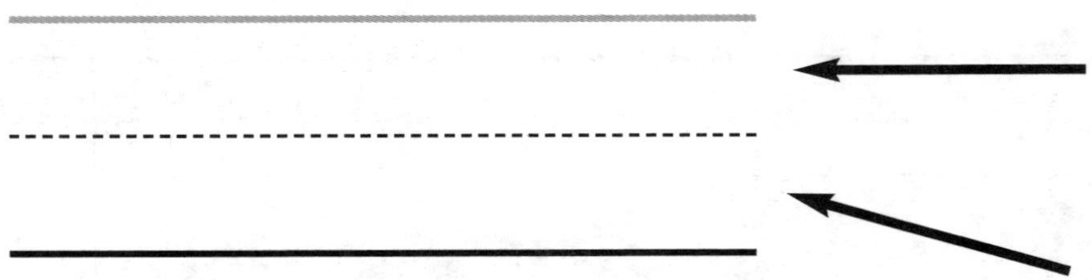

Between the dotted middle guide line and the light top guide line is the **upper space**.

Between the dotted middle guide line and the dark bottom guide line is the **lower space**.

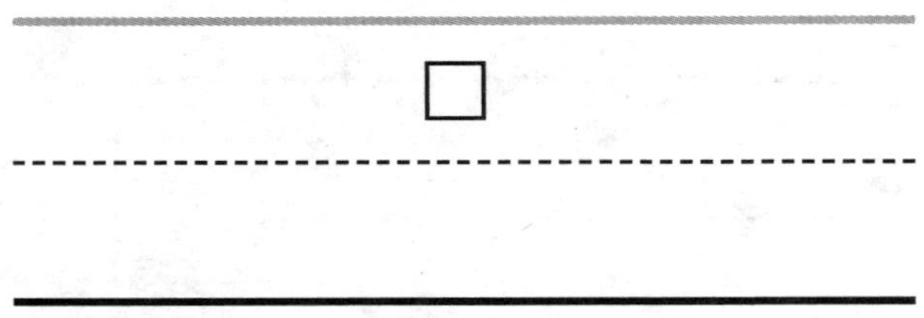

The square is in the middle of the **upper space**. It is not closer to the dotted middle guide line or the light top guide line.

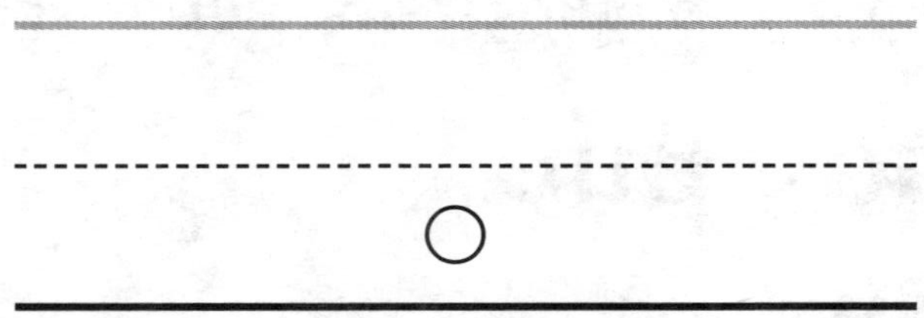

The circle is in the middle of the **lower space**. It is just as far away from the dotted middle guide line as it is from the dark bottom guide line. Both the square and the circle are in the middle of a space on the guide lines.

The Middle of Spaces and Forward Hook Strokes *(cont.)*

Look at the dots. Some are in the middle of the upper space, and some are in the middle of the lower space.

Can you put more dots in the middle of the upper space?

Can you put more dots in the middle of the lower space?

The Middle of Spaces and Forward Hook Strokes *(cont.)*

Here is a new stroke. It looks like the umbrella handles we made except that it is upside down.

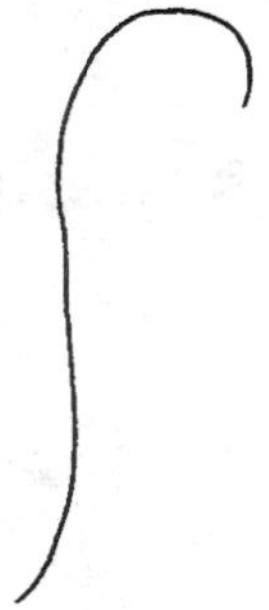

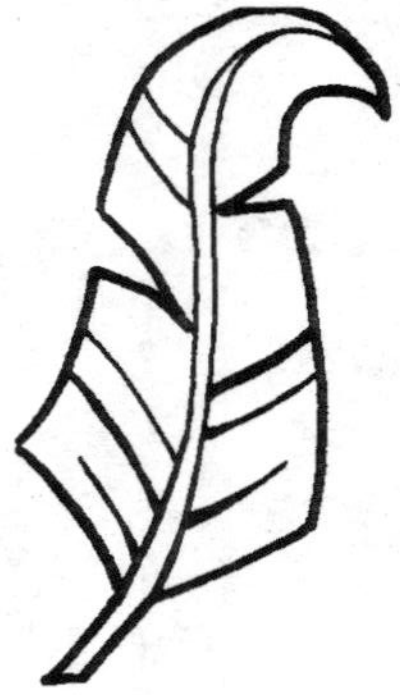

It looks like a feather. To make the feather hook stroke begin at the top, make the hook, and then pull straight down.

Here are some feathers. Can you make the stroke in the middle of the feather?

The Middle of Spaces and Forward Hook Strokes *(cont.)*

Here are some more feathers. You can practice the new feather hook stroke here.

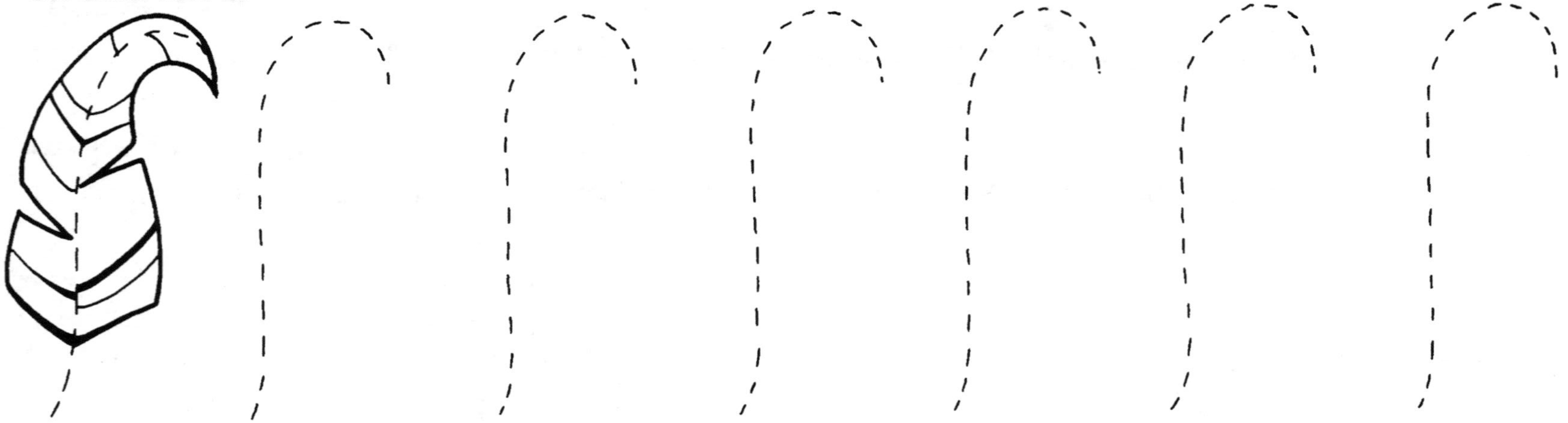

This hook stroke could be a candy cane, too.

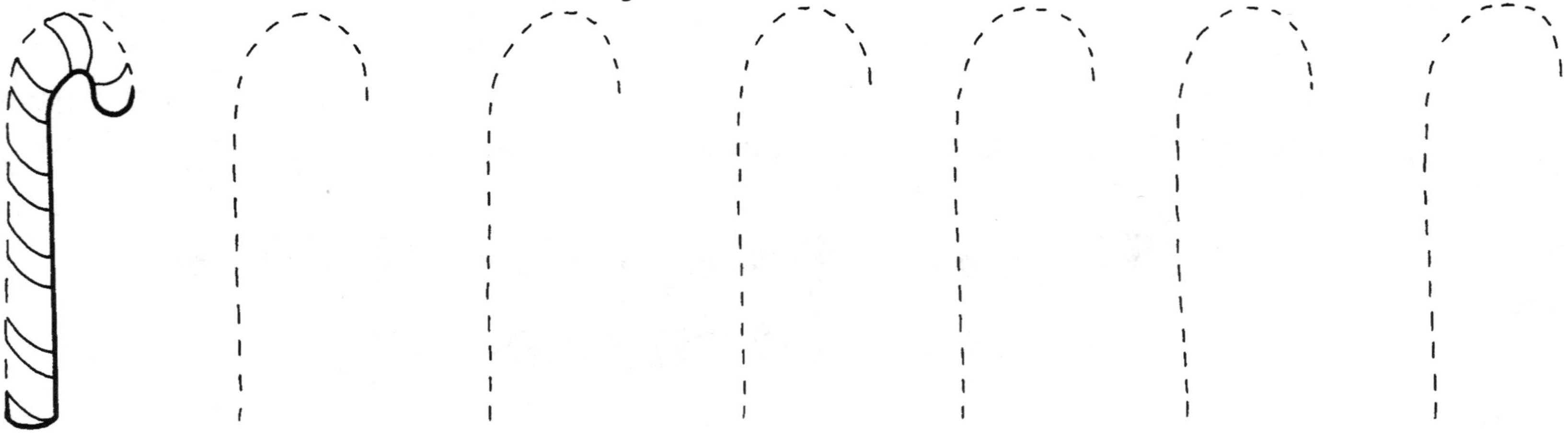

The Middle of Spaces and Forward Hook Strokes *(cont.)*

Here are some of the feather hook strokes on guide lines. Trace them with your pencil. Do you see something special about the place that each feather hook stroke begins?

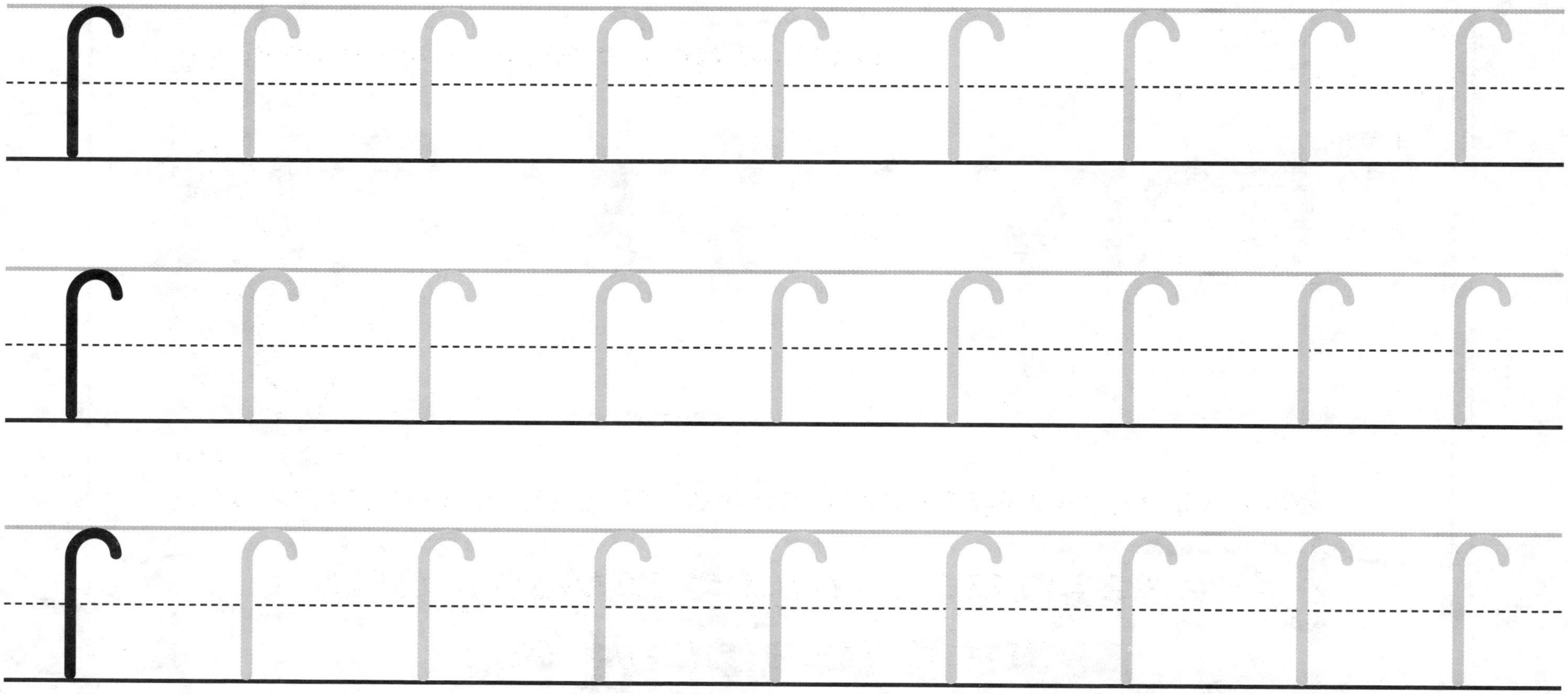

Section 4

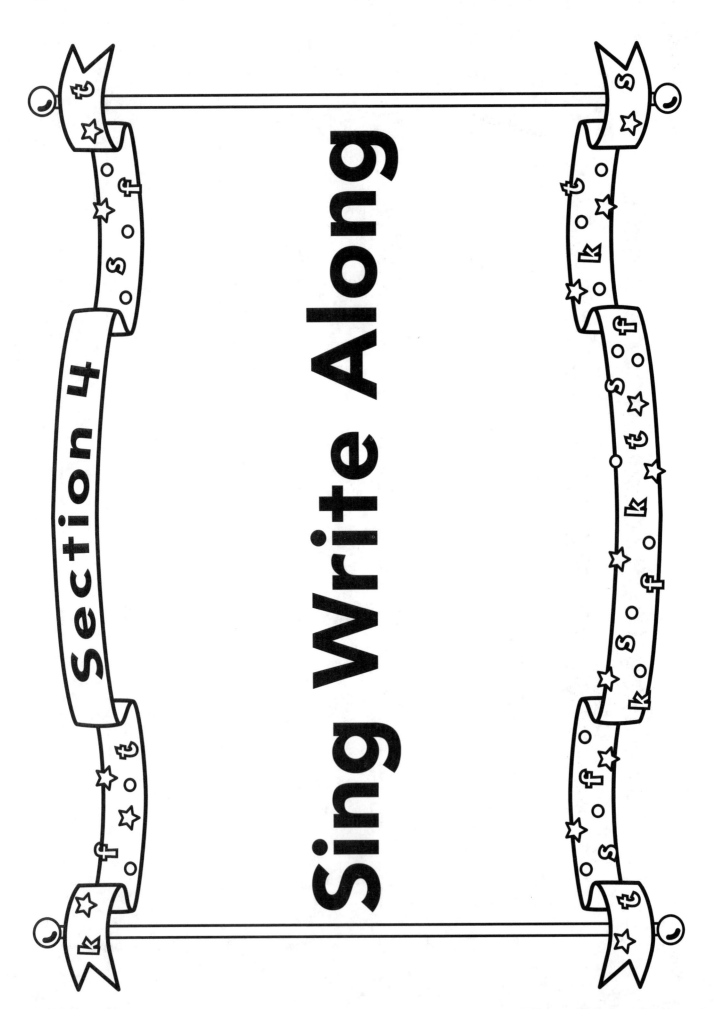

Sing Write Along

Teaching the Letters k, f, t, and s

Write Rhymes Poster for the Letters l and k

l k l

Two more letters that I know
Are long ones, l and k.
l stands very straight and tall
But k, it walks away.

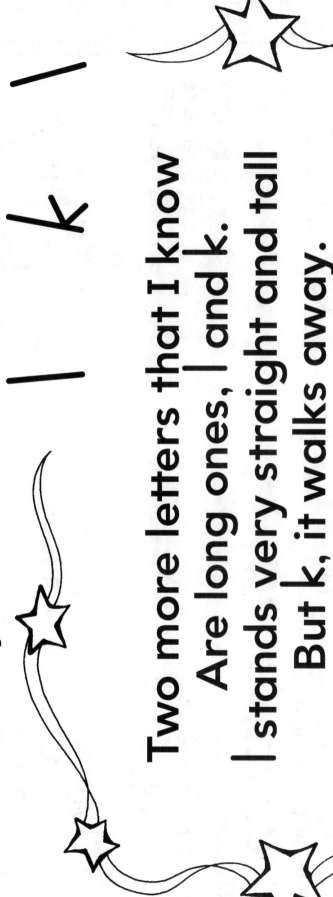

k l k

Teaching the Letters k, f, t, and s *(cont.)*

You learned the letter **l** a long time ago. Our next letter, **k**, begins just like the letter **l**. You will start at the light top guide line and make a straight line all the way to the dark bottom guide line. Then you will add some slanted lines to write the letter **k**. But you will have to look carefully to find the right place for these slanted lines.

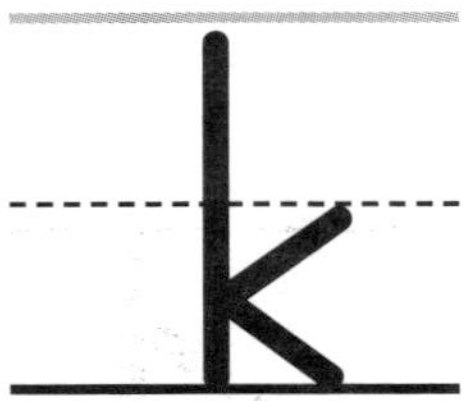

Find the middle of the lower space. Now put a tiny dot in the middle of the lower space, right on the line that you already wrote. That's where your slanted lines will go.

You will draw one slanted line from the dotted middle guide line to your dot and another slanted line from your dot to the dark bottom guide line. That is the letter **k**!

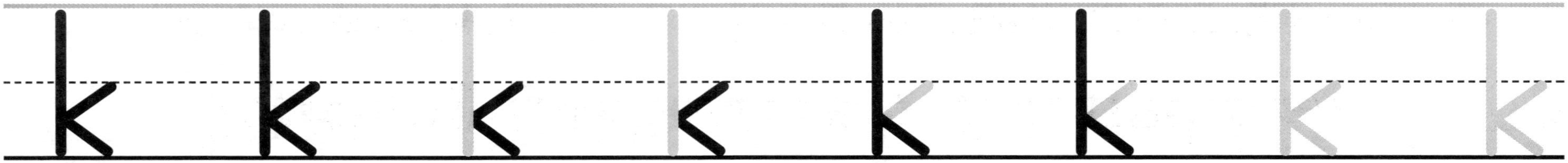

Teaching the Letters k, f, t, and s *(cont.)*

Let's try writing the letter **k**. Here the lines are made for you and the dot is in just the right place. Practice writing the line that goes from the dotted middle guide line to exactly the right place in the middle of the lower space.

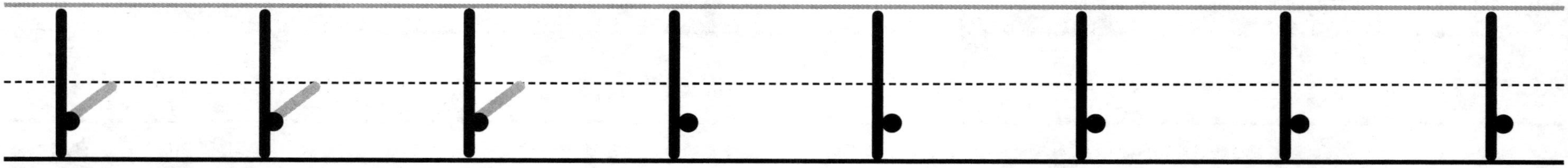

Now you can practice writing the second slanted line that goes from the dot to the dark bottom guide line.

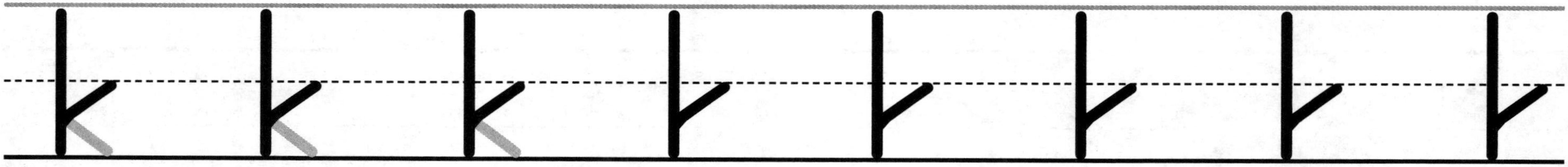

Let's try writing both slanted lines to write the letter **k**!

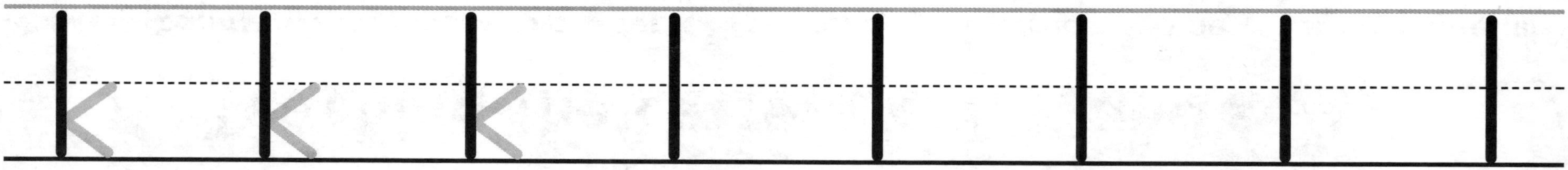

Teaching the Letters k, f, t, and s *(cont.)*

Now you can try writing the whole letter **k**. You can begin by tracing some. Then try some all by yourself.

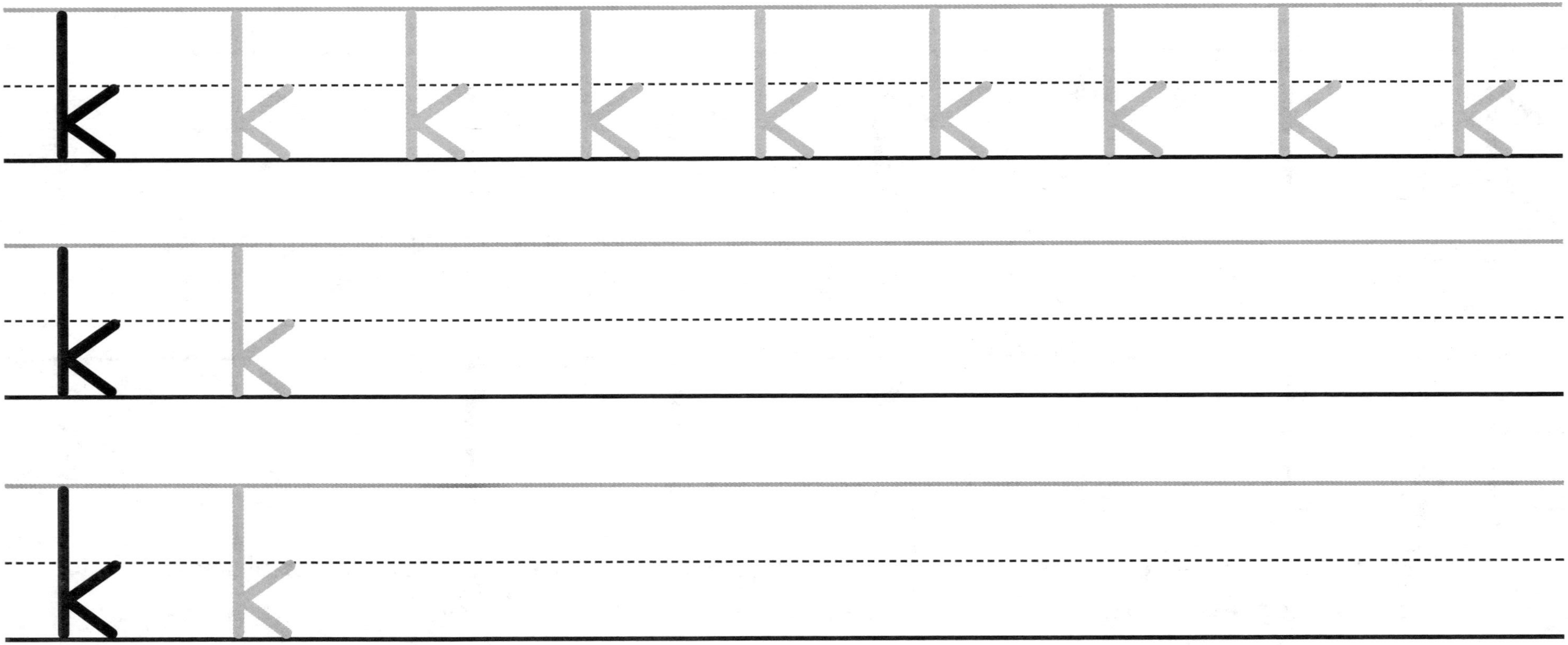

The letter **k** is one of the hardest letters to learn. If you need more practice, ask your teacher to give you the Ghost Paper (page 270) for the letter k or a piece of Guide Paper (page 287), so you can practice.

Teaching the Letters k, f, t, and s *(cont.)*

Write Rhymes Poster for the Letters f and t

f and t, I watch to see
That they cross on the line.
f is like a candy cane,
And t is straight and fine.

Teaching the Letters k, f, t, and s *(cont.)*

When you were learning the new feather hook stroke you practiced making a candy cane, too. That candy cane is the beginning of the new letter **f**.

To write the letter **f**, you must first find the middle of the upper space. That is where the hook stroke begins. Then you will curve up and backward until you reach the light top guide line. Keep curving and begin to come down.

The rest is easy. Keep going and make a straight line all the way to the dark bottom guide line. Then the hook stroke is done and you will only have to add the last part, which is a small straight line that crosses the hook stroke and sits right on the dotted middle guide line.

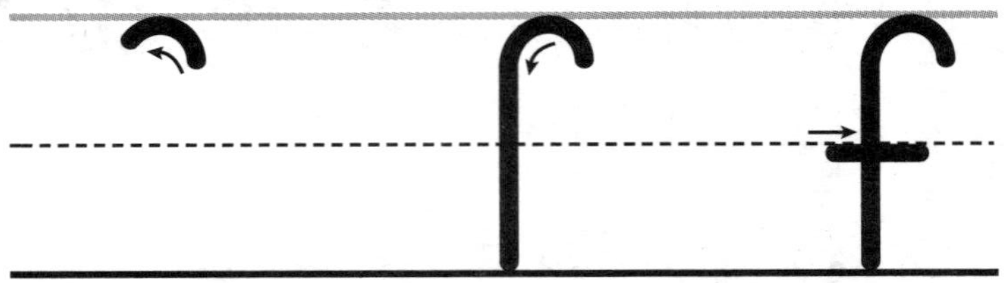

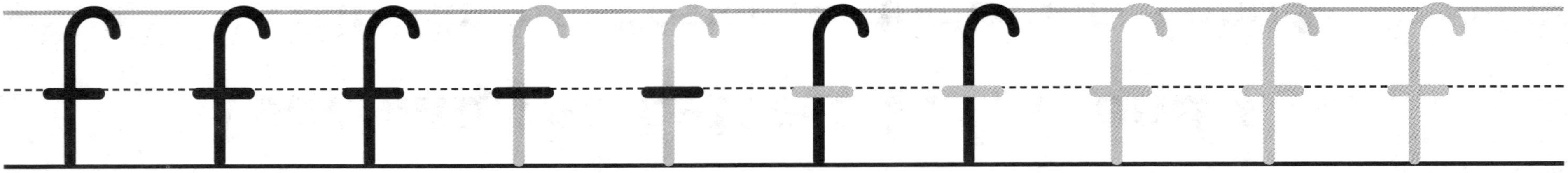

Teaching the Letters k, f, t, and s *(cont.)*

Here are some hook strokes that have already been made for you. You can practice writing the line that crosses the hook stroke. This line, or crossbar, finishes the letter **f**.

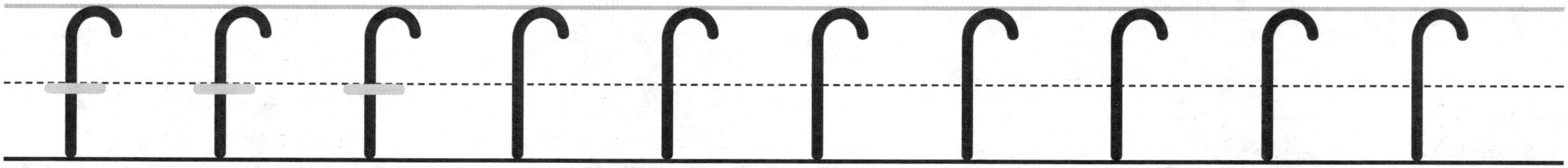

Now let's practice both the strokes that make the letter **f**. Say the name of the letter as you write it.

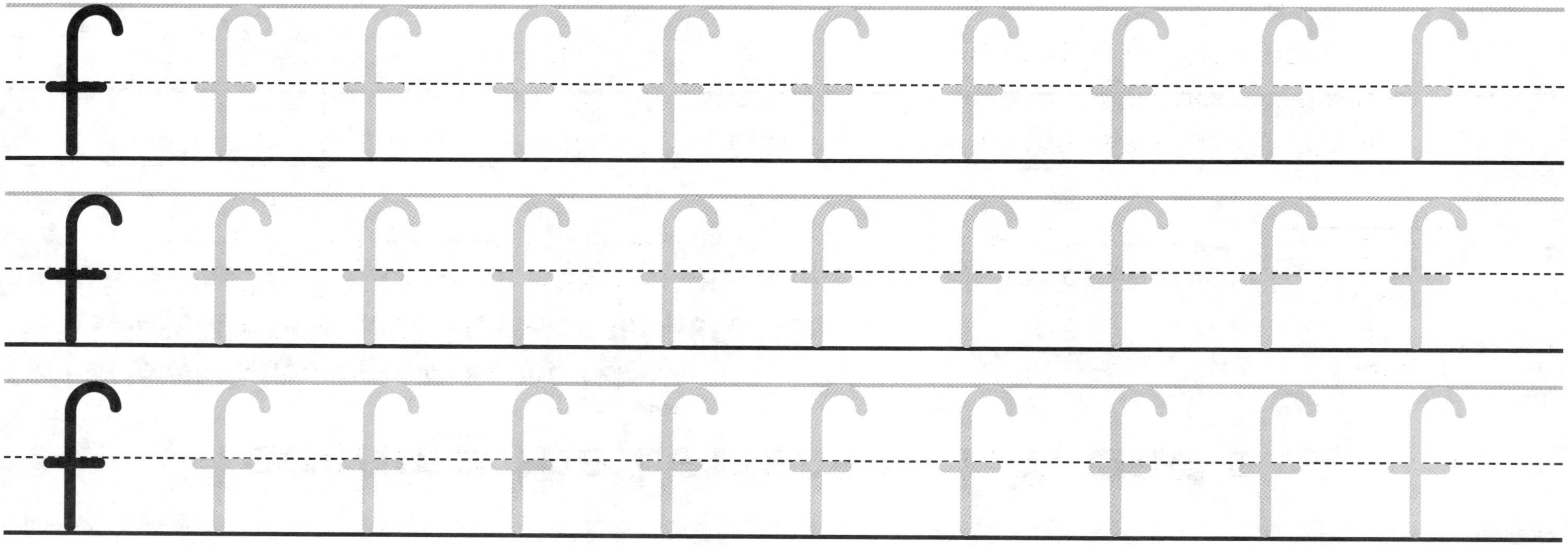

Teaching the Letters k, f, t, and s *(cont.)*

Do not let your hook stroke be too skinny. f

Do not let your hook stroke be too wide either. f

Now write the letter f all by yourself. Say the name of the letter as you write it.

f f

f f

f f

f f

Teaching the Letters k, f, t, and s *(cont.)*

Let's practice both of the new letters (**k** and **f**) we have learned. Say the name of each letter as you write it.

k k

f f

k f k f

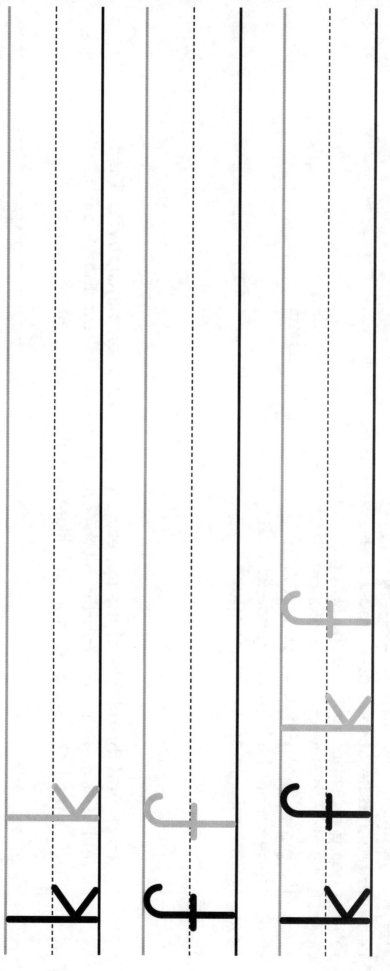

You need to use the middle of a space to make each of these letters. The letter **k** uses the middle of the lower space.

Teaching the Letters k, f, t, and s *(cont.)*

The next letter, **t**, is so easy to do now that you can find the middle of the upper space. The letter t has a crossbar just like the letter **f** does, but it does not have any hooks at all. It is as straight as an **l**, but it is not as tall. It does not begin on the light top guide line. It beings in the middle of the upper space.

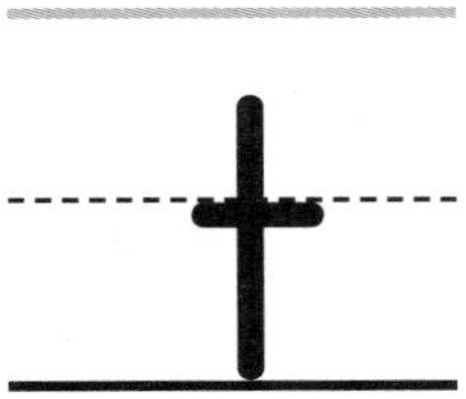

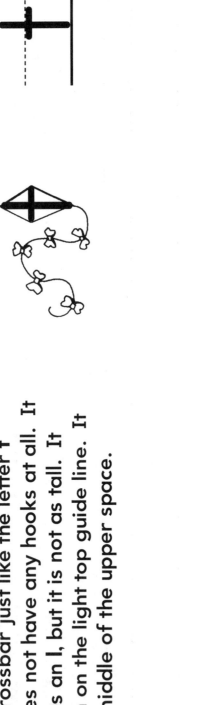

First, find the middle of the upper space and put your pencil there. Then pull down, nice and straight, all the way to the dark bottom guide line. Then give the letter **t** a crossbar, just like the letter **f**, and you are done!

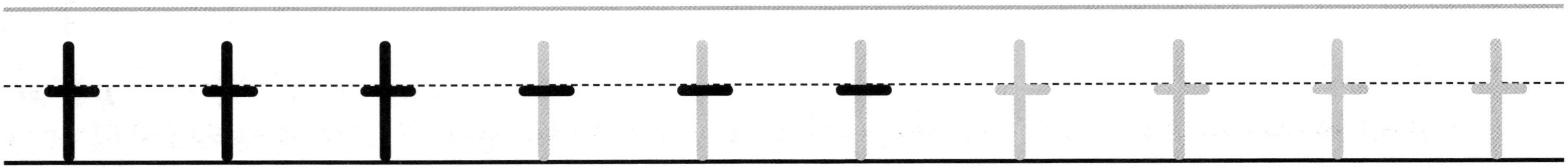

Teaching the Letters k, f, t, and s *(cont.)*

Here is a page for you to practice the letter t. Say the name of the letter as you write it.

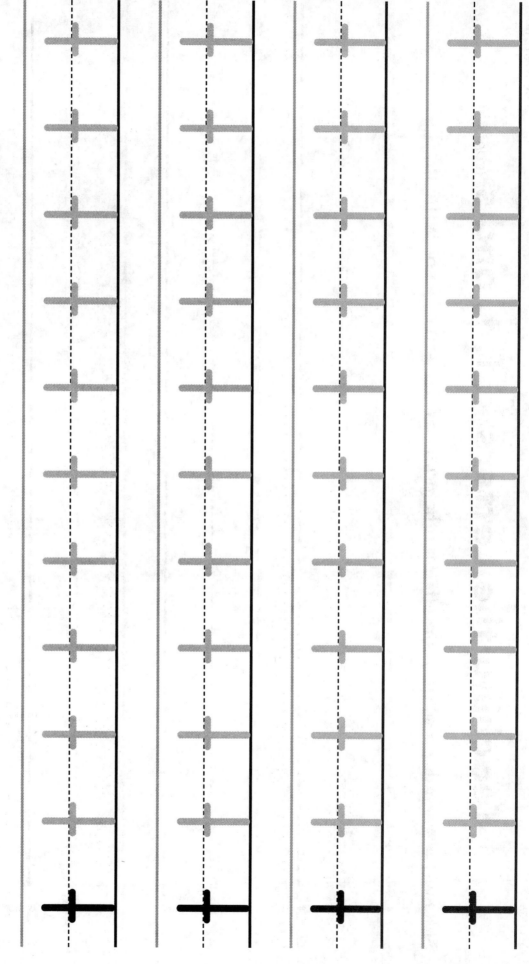

Teaching the Letters k, f, t, and s *(cont.)*

Now write the letter t all by yourself! Say the name of the letter as you write it.

t t

t t

t t

t t

Teaching the Letters k, f, t, and s *(cont.)*

All three of these letters (**k**, **f**, and **t**) need the middle of a space. Do not forget to say the name of each letter as you write it.

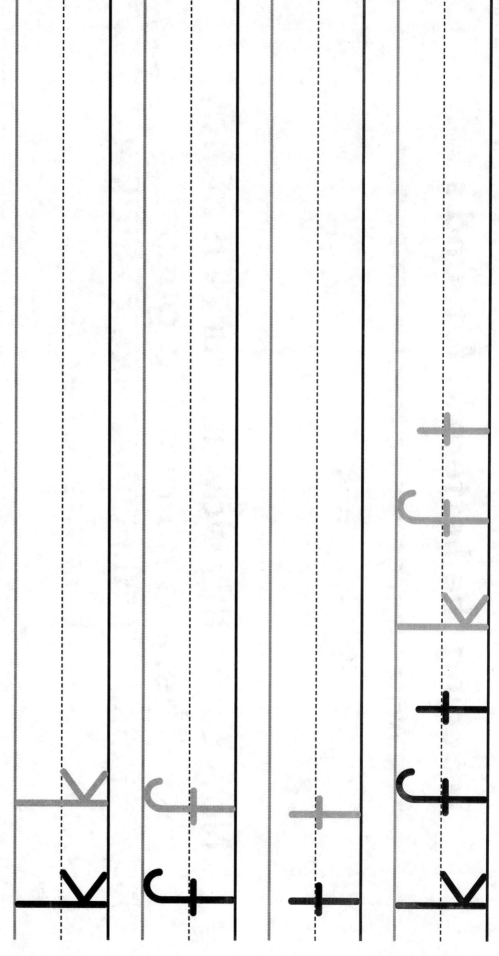

k k

f f

t t

k f t k f t

Teaching the Letters k, f, t, and s *(cont.)*

Write Rhymes Poster for the Letter s

s s s

Now curve this way and curve that way
There is no need to guess.
It curls around just like a snake;
It is the letter s.

s s s

Teaching the Letters k, f, t, and s *(cont.)*

Here is the new letter **s**. You may need some extra practice making this letter because it is very curvy.

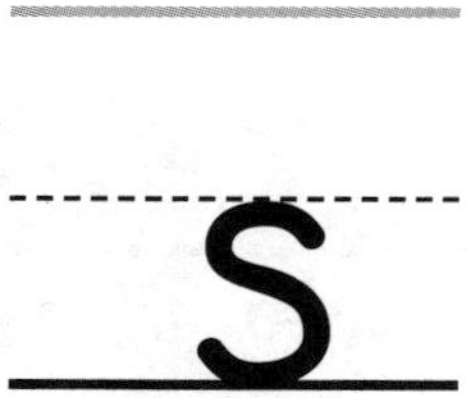

It begins in a new place. It begins just under the dotted middle guide line but not in the middle. Then it curves up like a feather stroke, but it does not have a straight part. It keeps curving! It changes direction in the middle of the lower space and curves the other way!

If we made the letter **s** really big on guide lines, it would look a little like the letter **c** in the upper space and a backward **c** in the lower space!

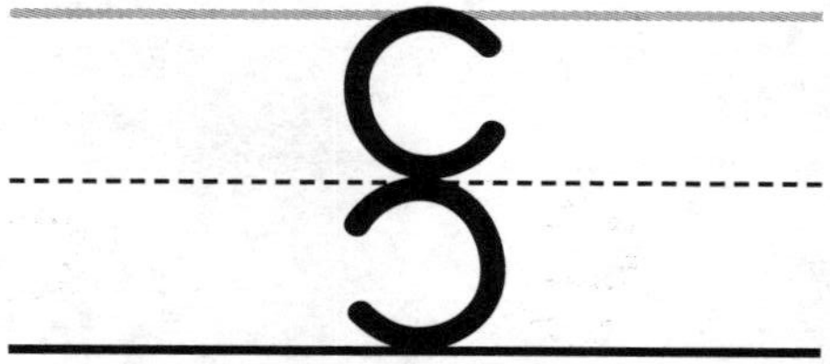

Finish writing the letter **s**.

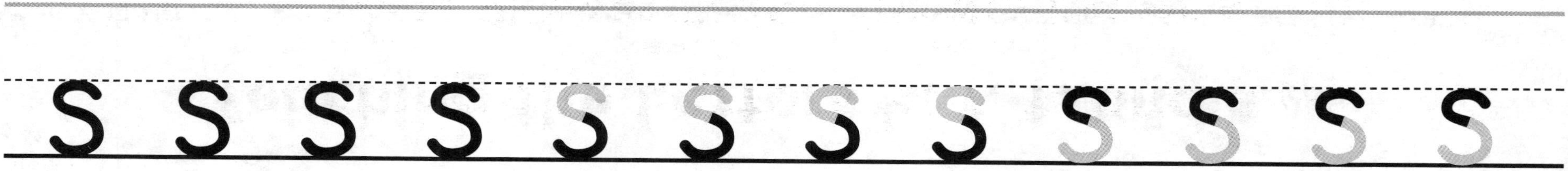

Teaching the Letters k, f, t, and s *(cont.)*

You will have to be extra careful because the letter **s** is little and only goes from the dotted middle guide line to the dark bottom guide line. Start under the dotted middle guide line, curve around, and then start back the other way. Curve to touch the dark bottom guide line, and then start to come back up again — and then stop!

s s s s s s s s s s s s

s s s s s s s s s s s s

s s s s s s s s s s s s

Teaching the Letters k, f, t, and s *(cont.)*

Now write the letter s all by yourself. Say the name of the letter as you write it. There is Ghost Paper (page 278) if you need more practice with the letter s.

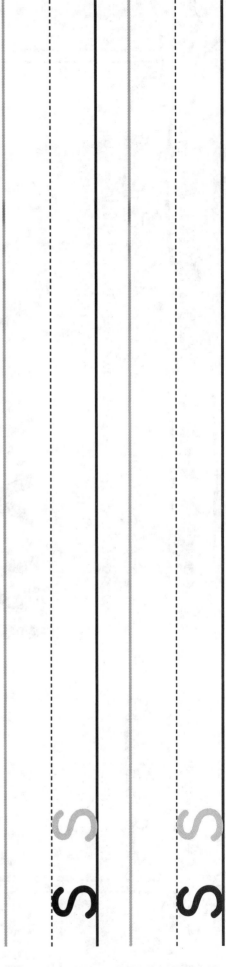

s s

s s

s s

s s

Section 4

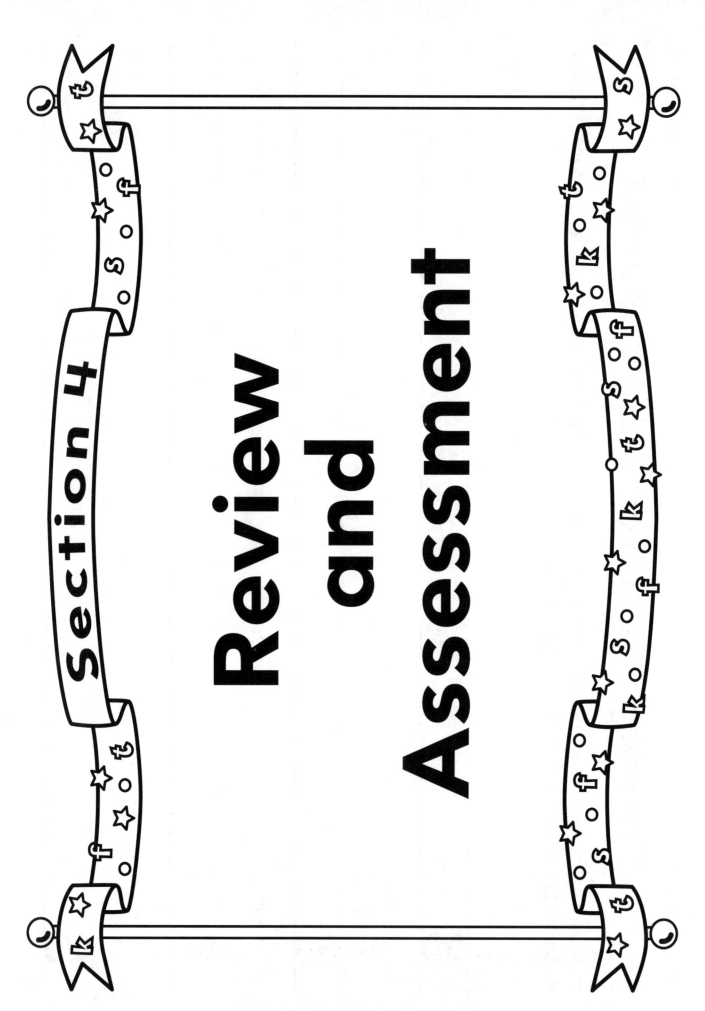

Review and Assessment

Cumulative Review and Assessment

Here is a place to review the four letters that we have just learned. Write the letters **k**, **f**, **t**, and **s**. Say the name of each letter as you write it.

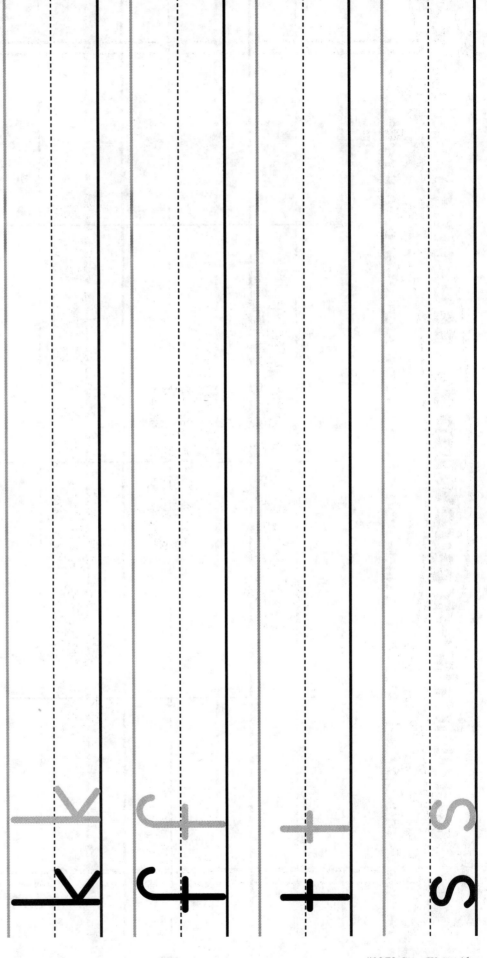

k k

f f

t t

s s

Cumulative Review and Assessment *(cont.)*

Now let's mix up the letters k, f, t, and s. Say the name of each letter as you write it.

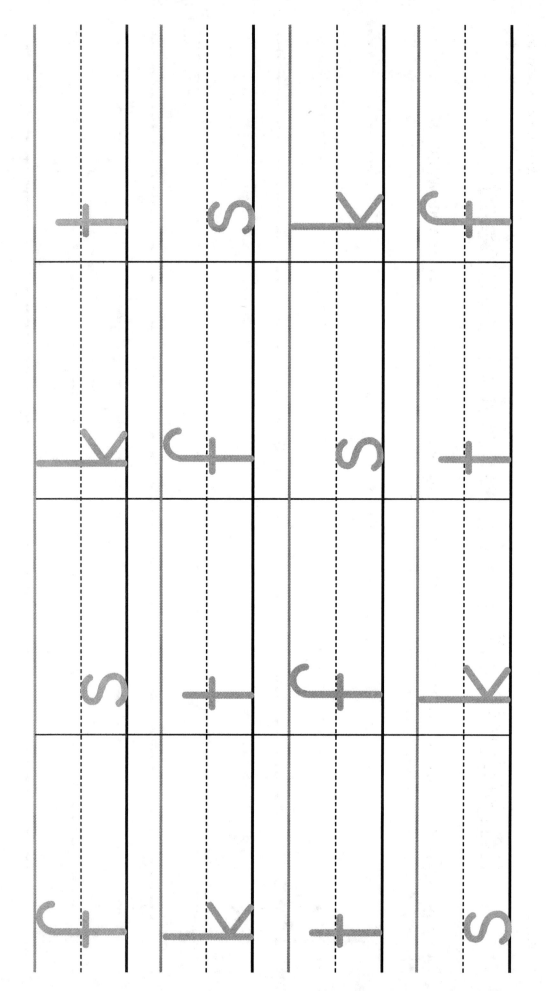

f	s	k	t
k	t	f	s
t	f	s	k
s	k	t	f

Cumulative Review and Assessment *(cont.)*

Do you remember all the letters that use slanted lines? Say each letter as you write it.

v	x	y	w
z	y	v	x
w	z	y	v
z	v	x	w

Cumulative Review and Assessment *(cont.)*

Here are some letters you know well. Let's practice them, too. Say the name of each letter as you write it.

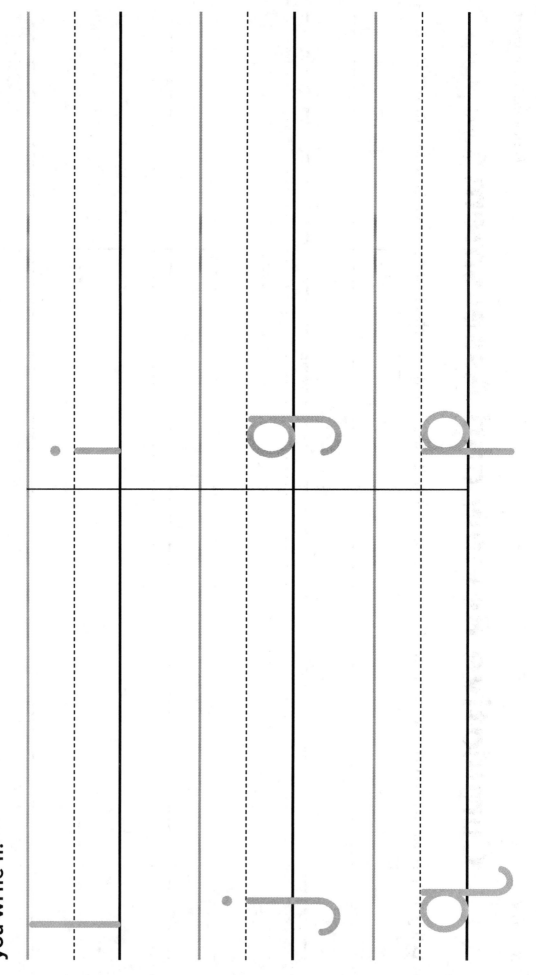

l	i
j	g
q	p

Cumulative Review and Assessment *(cont.)*

These are the letters you learned a long time ago! Say the name of each letter as you write it.

o a

c e

b d

Cumulative Review and Assessment *(cont.)*

Now you know most of the letters in the alphabet! We'll practice them all! Say the name of each letter as you write it.

j	z	b	e
a	k	s	y
f	o	w	t
d	v	x	c

Cumulative Review and Assessment *(cont.)*

Can you say the names of all these letters as you write them?

p	t	y	q
z	d	s	j
i	k	g	f
e	b	w	l

Cumulative Review and Assessment *(cont.)*

Look back over pages 208 and 209. Look carefully at each letter that you have written. Use a crayon to circle the letters that you think are your very best and show those to your teacher.

Now look carefully at all your letters again. Check the sizes of the letters and look at where they are placed on the guide lines. Are your straight lines very straight? Do the circles and curves look just as they should?

If you see any that are not just the way you want them to be, you may want to use Ghost Paper (pages 260–266, 268–271, 274–276, 278, 279, 281–285) to practice those letters until you are proud of each and every one. As you practice, you will get better and better at making each letter look just the way you want it to.

When you are happy with all of your letters, you will be ready to go on.

Get ready to show off!

Cumulative Review and Assessment *(cont.)*

Here are the letters k, f, t, and s that Tani has written. They are her very best letters. Make your very best letters, too.

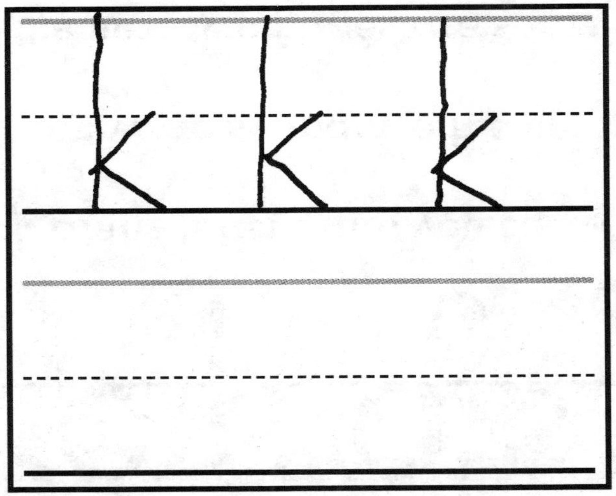

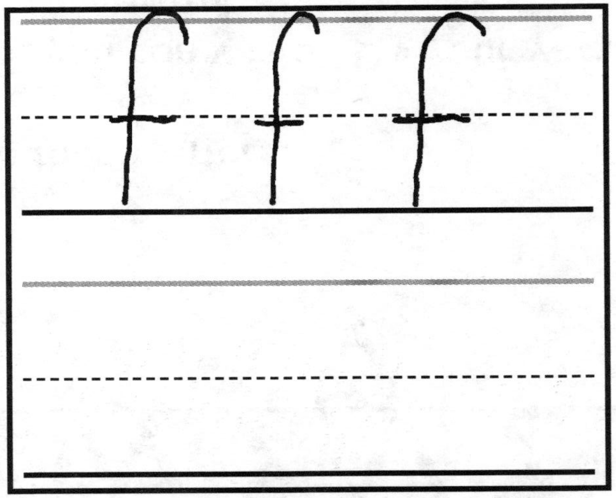

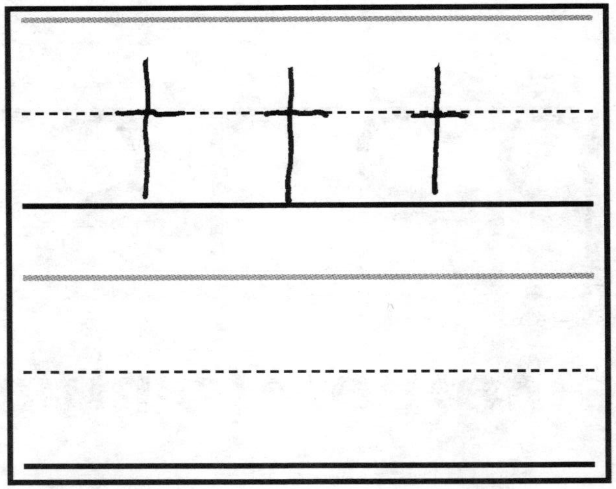

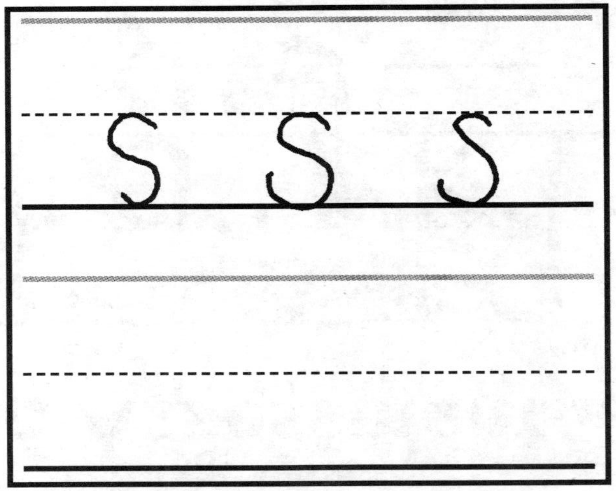

Cumulative Review and Assessment *(cont.)*

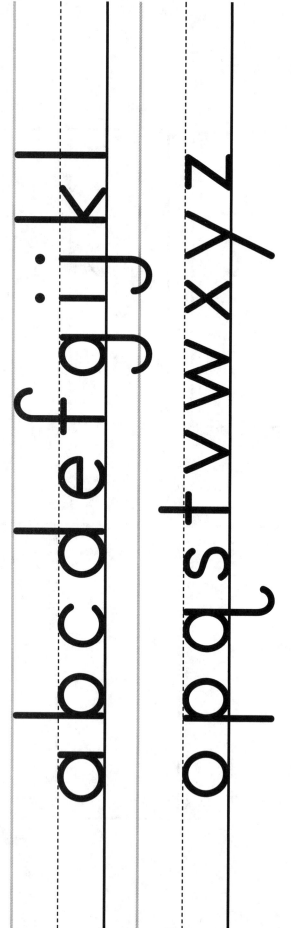

a b c d e f g i j k l

o p q s t v w x y z

Look at the letters that you can write!

You can write so many different words with these letters!

On the next two pages are some words that you can write. Do your very best and neatest work. Take your time and be careful.

Remember to use our songs to help you remember how to write the letters.

Get ready to show off!

Cumulative Review and Assessment *(cont.)*

Write these words.

sit	vest
wide	web
zest	kit
pick	flip

Cumulative Review and Assessment *(cont.)*

Write these words.

exit	tack
bold	cast
stop	jog
play	zap

Section 5

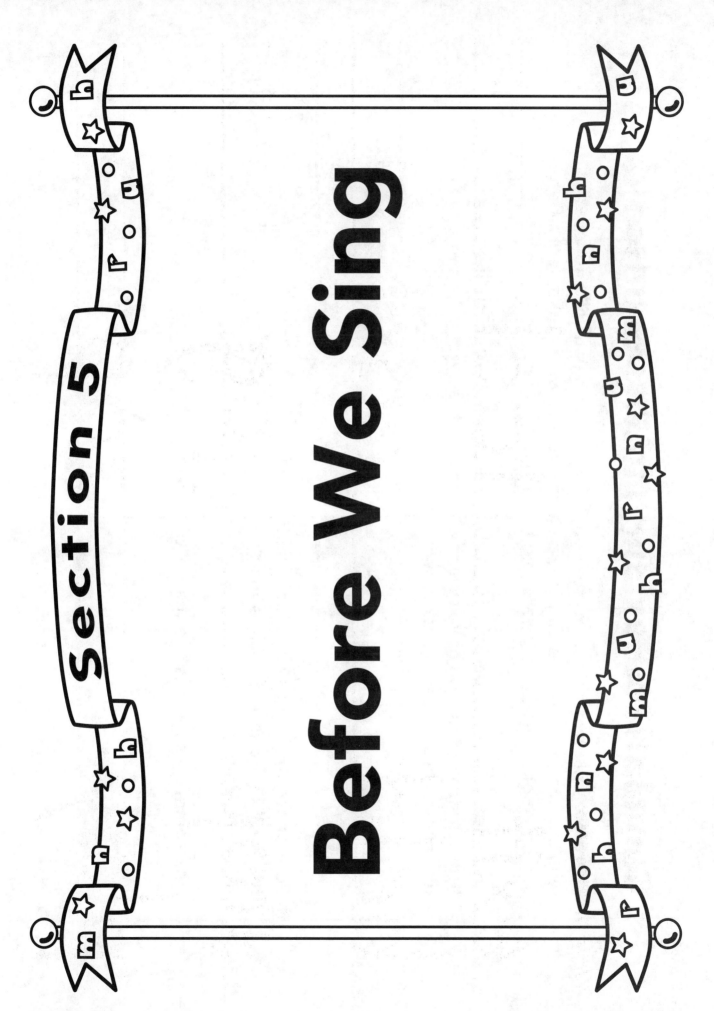

Before We Sing

Reverse Hooks and Downward Hooks

There are only five letters left for you to learn. Then you will know the whole alphabet. There is only one new stroke you will need to learn before you can make these five letters and that is the hook stroke.

This hook stroke will be easy to learn because it is very much like the feather stroke that you have already learned. It just goes the other way and sometimes it goes upside down!

Sometimes the hook stroke looks like the hook at the top of a Christmas tree ornament.

And sometimes it looks like the tail of a seahorse.

Reverse Hooks and Downward Hooks *(cont.)*

Can you make the hooks on all these ornaments? Remember to start at the top, make the hook, and pull down.

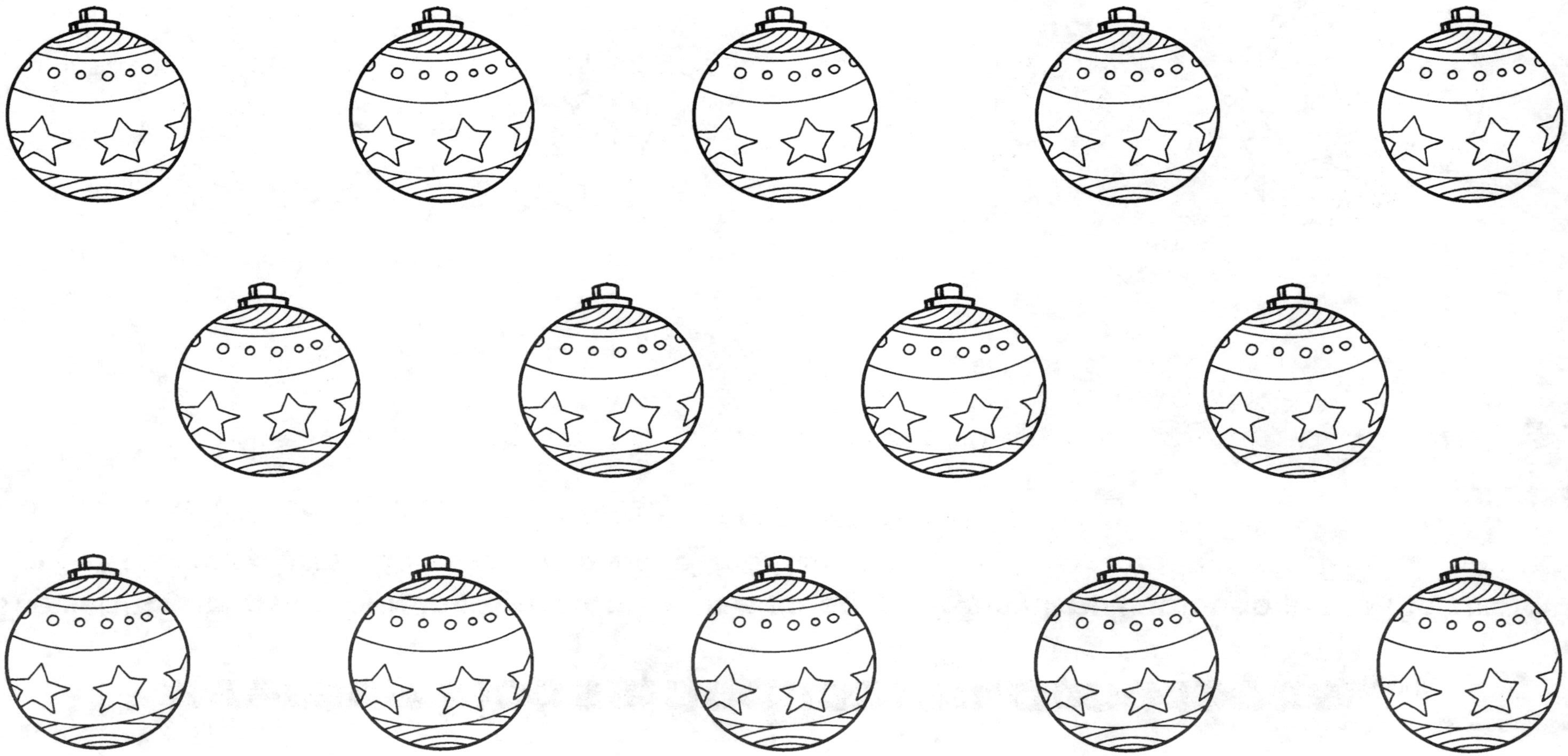

Reverse Hooks and Downward Hooks *(cont.)*

The seahorse has a hook that goes down instead of up. You will pull down to make the straight part of the hook first, then the curve will come last.

Can you put tails on all these seahorses?

Reverse Hooks and Downward Hooks *(cont.)*

Let's practice these hooks on some guide lines.

Make ornament hooks here.

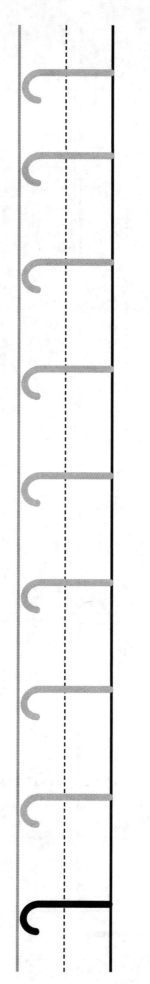

And try some seahorse hooks here.

Reverse Hooks and Downward Hooks *(cont.)*

Now let's work on making some little hooks. They will only reach from the dotted middle guide line to the dark bottom guide line.

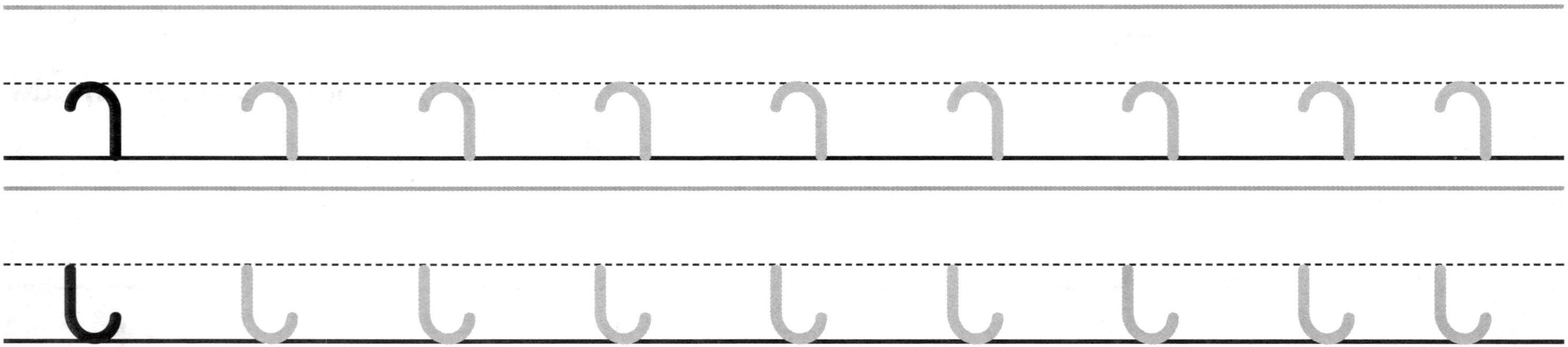

Now let's try both big and little hooks!

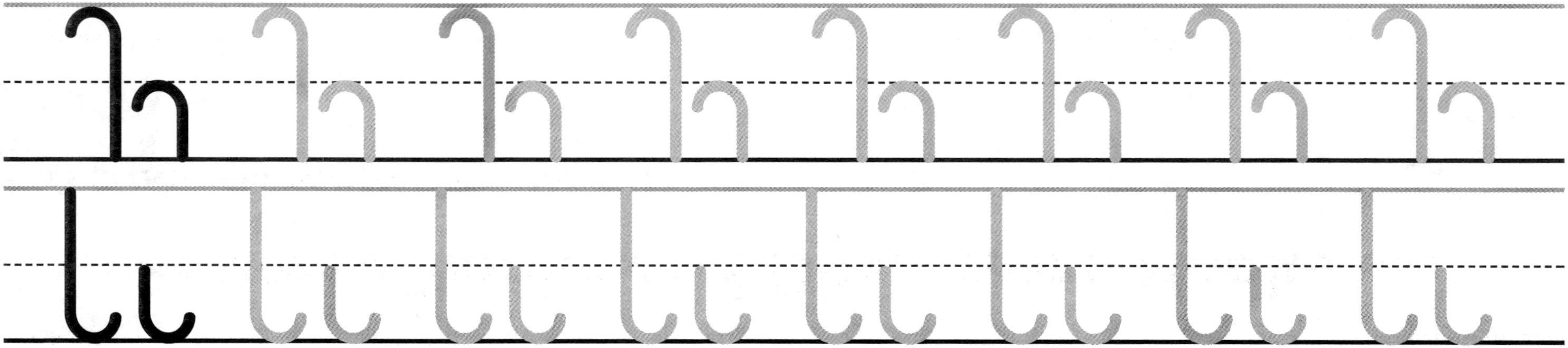

Reverse Hooks and Downward Hooks *(cont.)*

Can you make some hooks by yourself?

Section 5

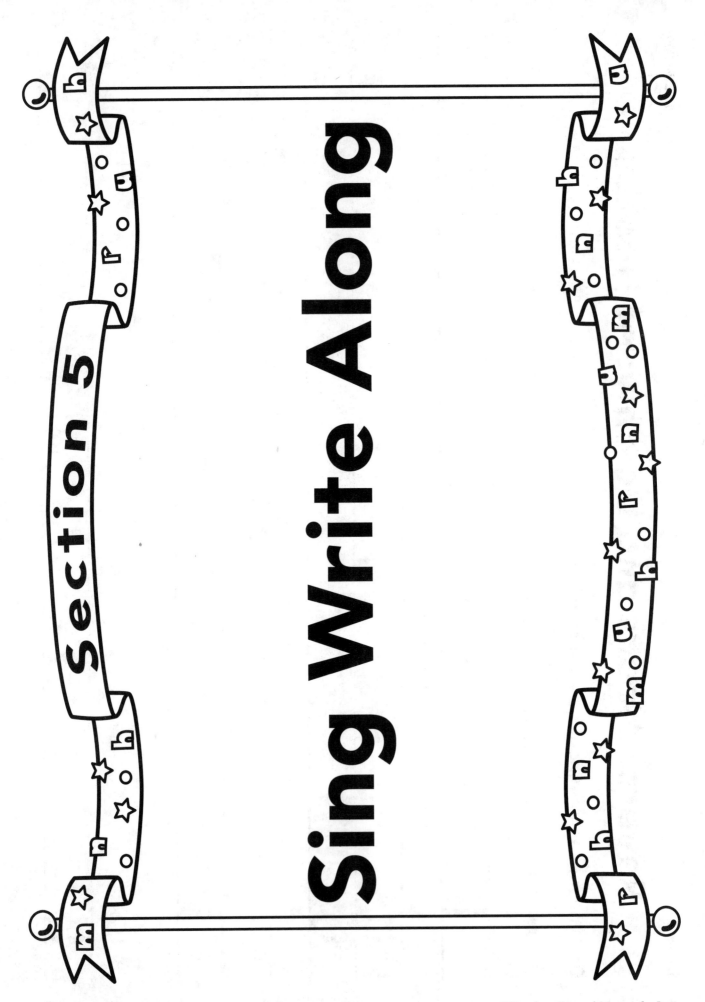

Sing Write Along

Teaching the Letters **n**, **m**, **h**, **r**, and **u**

Write Rhymes Poster for the Letters **n** and **m**

m n m

If you mix up n and m
I'll say you are to blame.
n has one hook, m has two,
And so they're not the same.

n m n

Teaching the Letters n, m, h, r, and u *(cont.)*

Here is Nolan the turtle. His letter is the new letter **n**. The new letter will begin with a short, straight line and then you will add a hook to finish the letter **n**. The hook is like the ornament hook that we have already learned.

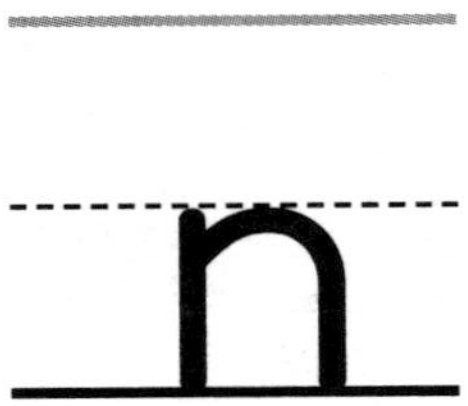

The curved part of the hook will touch the short, straight line and that makes the letter **n**. It is a short letter and will fit between the dotted middle guide line and the dark bottom guide line.

Finish writing the letter **n**.

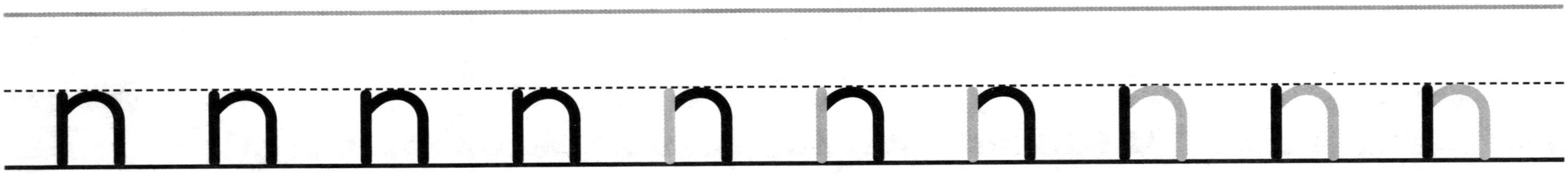

Teaching the Letters n, m, h, r, and u *(cont.)*

When you make the letter **n**, remember to begin your hook right up against the straight line that you wrote. Put your pencil on the straight line just under the dotted middle guide line. Then bring your hook up to touch the dotted middle guide line and back down to the dark bottom guide line.

n n n n

n n n n n n n n n n

n n n n n n n n n n

Teaching the Letters n, m, h, r, and u *(cont.)*

Now write the letter **n** all by yourself. Say the name of the letter as you write it.

n n

n n

n n

n n

Teaching the Letters n, m, h, r, and u *(cont.)*

Marty the clown has the new letter **m**. It looks a lot like **n**, but it is not the same.

You will begin with an **n** when you write Marty's letter, but you will add another hook to change the **n** into the letter **m**. It is an **n** when you begin, but the second hook changes it from **n** to **m**.

m

Make sure you begin the second hook under the dotted middle guide line, right on the first hook.

m m m m m m m

Finish writing the letter **m**.

m m m m m m m

Teaching the Letters n, m, h, r, and u *(cont.)*

Try to keep both hooks the same size. Do not let the letter **m** be too skinny. **m** Do not let the letter **m** be too fat. **m** Do not let the hooks on the letter **m** be two different sizes.

Here is a place where you can practice writing the letter **m**.

m m m m m m m

m m m m m m m

m m m m m m m

Teaching the Letters n, m, h, r, and u *(cont.)*

Now write the letter **m** all by yourself. Say the name of the letter as you write it!

m m

m m

m m

m m

Teaching the Letters n, m, h, r, and u *(cont.)*

Let's practice n and m together. Can you tell which is which?

n n

m m

m n m n

n m n m

Teaching the Letters n, m, h, r, and u *(cont.)*

Write Rhymes Poster for the Letter h

h, it also has a hook
And looks quite like the others,
You make it with a big, long stem;
I guess that they are brothers.

Teaching the Letters n, m, h, r, and u *(cont.)*

Here is the letter **h** with Helen the giraffe. It is easy to write the letter **h** because it is so much like the letter **n**.

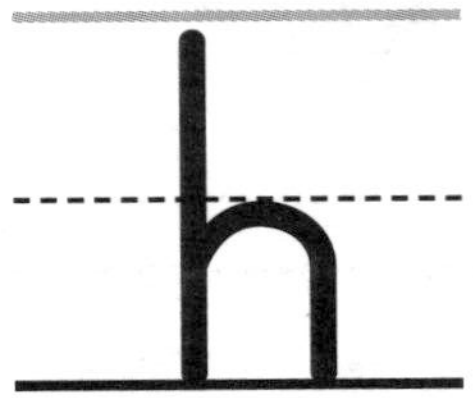

Begin the letter **h** with a long, straight line instead of a short one. Begin the line at the light top guide line and bring it all the way down to the dark bottom guide line, just like writing the letter **l**. Then you add the ornament hook, but put it in the bottom space, just like the letter **n**. Then you have made the letter **h**!

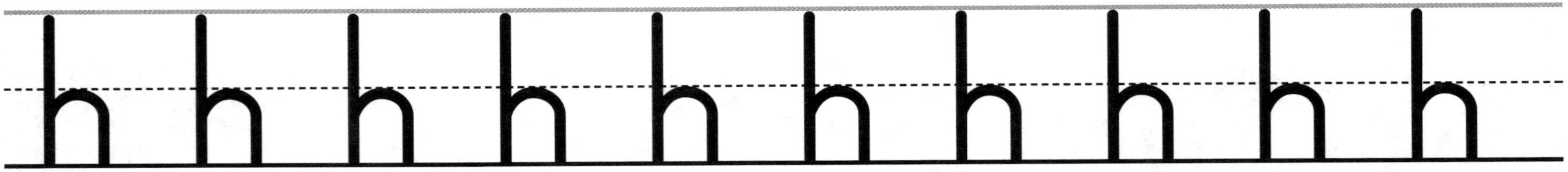

Finish writing the letter **h**.

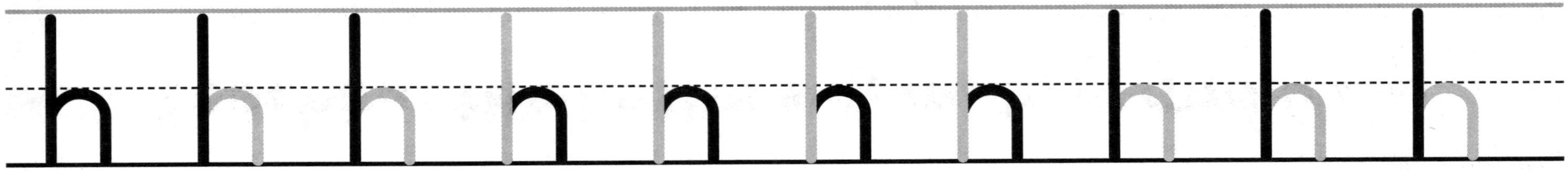

Teaching the Letters n, m, h, r, and u *(cont.)*

Here is a place to practice writing the letter **h**. Say the name of the letter as you write it.

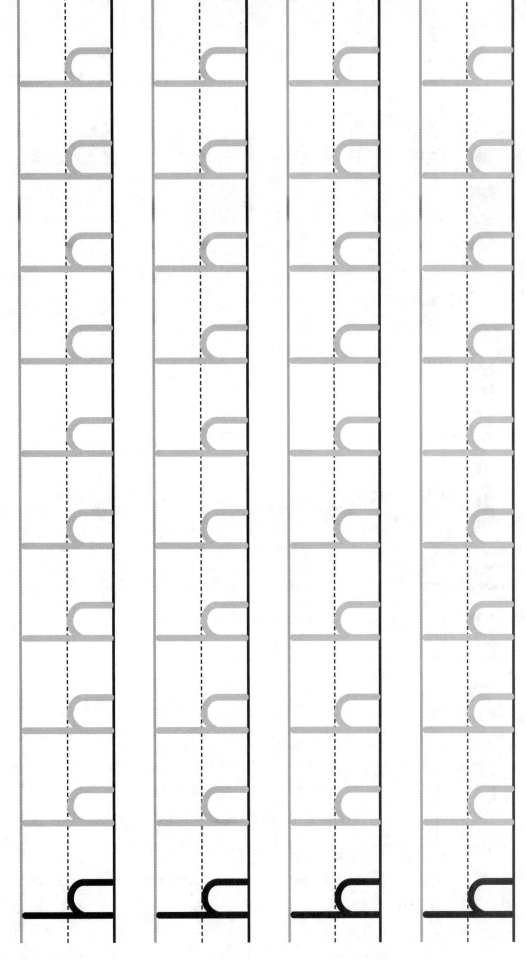

h h h h h h h h h h

h h h h h h h h h h

h h h h h h h h h h

h h h h h h h h h h

Teaching the Letters n, m, h, r, and u *(cont.)*

Now you can practice writing the letter **h** all by yourself. Be sure to say the name of the letter as you write it.

h h

h h

h h

h h

Teaching the Letters n, m, h, r, and u *(cont.)*

Now let's practice writing our three new letters, n, m, and h. Say the name of each letter as you write it.

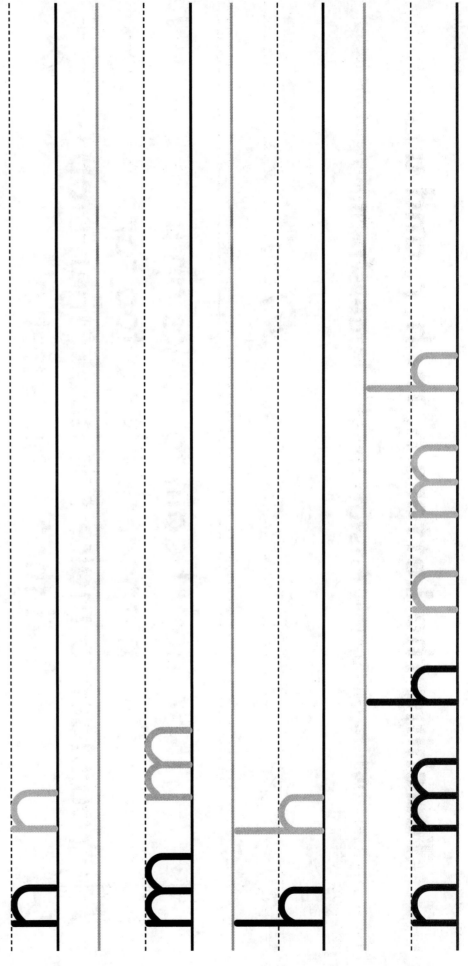

n n

m m

h h

n m h n m h

Teaching the Letters n, m, h, r, and u *(cont.)*

Write Rhymes Poster for the Letters n and r

r n r n r

So now begin to make an n
But, please, don't go too far.
You start to make the hook, then stop —
And that's the letter r!

r n r n r

Teaching the Letters n, m, h, r, and u *(cont.)*

Here is Rory the whale. His letter is the letter **r**. It is a lot like the letter **n**, too. Can you see how it is different?

r

To write the letter **r**, you will begin to make the letter **n**. Make the short, straight line and start to make the hook, but do not finish it! Stop the hook before you get to the middle of the bottom space.

That is the letter **r**!

r r r r r r r r r r r

Finish writing the letter **r**.

r r r r r r r r r r r

Teaching the Letters n, m, h, r, and u *(cont.)*

You can practice the letter **r** here. Say the name of the letter as you write it.

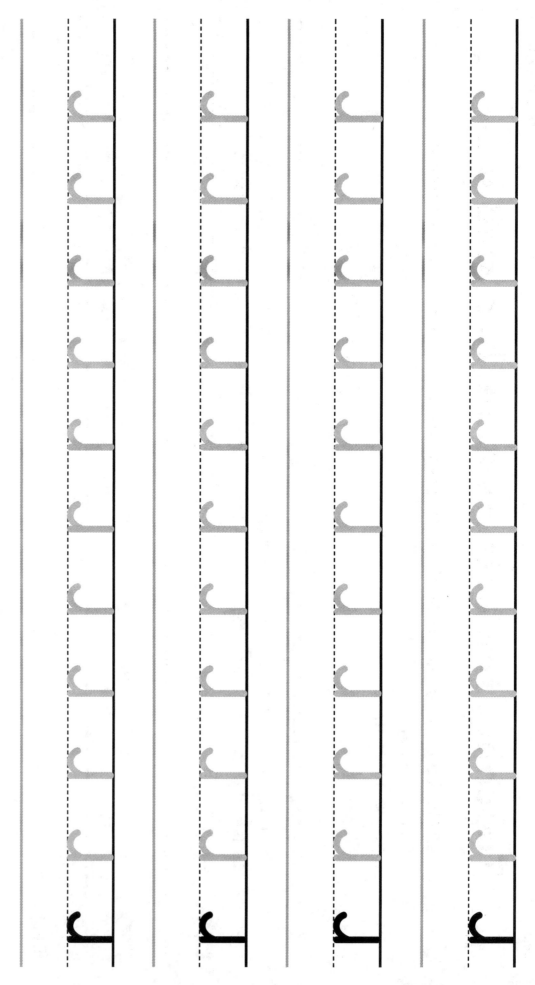

r r r r r r r r r r r

r r r r r r r r r r r

r r r r r r r r r r r

r r r r r r r r r r r

Teaching the Letters n, m, h, r, and u *(cont.)*

Now write the letter r all by yourself! Be sure to say the letter name as you write it.

r r

r r

r r

r r

Teaching the Letters n, m, h, r, and u *(cont.)*

Now let's practice all the new letters (**n**, **m**, **h**, and **r**).

n n

m m

h h

r r

There is only one more new letter to go!

Teaching the Letters n, m, h, r, and u *(cont.)*

The Write Rhymes Poster for the Letter **u**

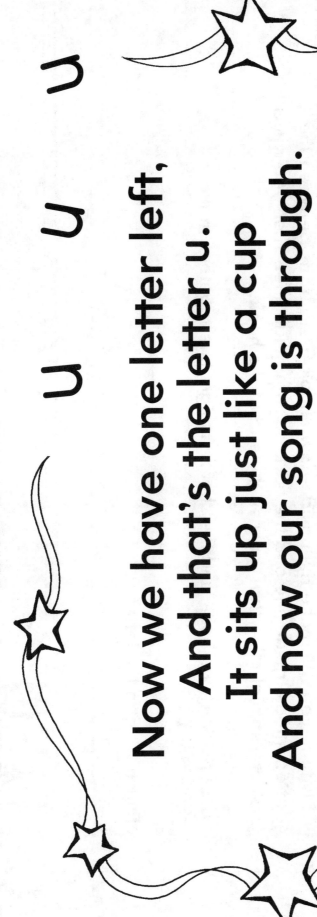

u u u

Now we have one letter left,
And that's the letter u.
It sits up just like a cup
And now our song is through.

u u u

Teaching the Letters n, m, h, r, and u *(cont.)*

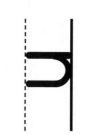

u

Here is a cup that makes the letter **u**. It is made with a hook like the one on the tail of the seahorse.

This time you will make the upside-down hook first. It fits between the dotted middle guide line and the dark bottom guide line. Then you will add a short, straight line that touches the end of the hook.

The upside-down hook and the short, straight line together make the letter **u**.

Finish writing the letter **u**.

u u u u u u u u u u

u u u u u u u u u u

Teaching the Letters n, m, h, r, and u *(cont.)*

Practice writing the letter **u**. Remember that the short, straight line must touch the tip of the hook. Do not let the line and the hook miss each other! Say the name of the letter as you write it.

u u u u u u u u u u

u u u u u u u u u u

u u u u u u u u u u

u u u u u u u u u u

Teaching the Letters n, m, h, r, and u *(cont.)*

Now practice the very last letter (u) all by yourself! Say the name of the letter as you write it.

u u

u u

u u

u u

Teaching the Letters n, m, h, r, and u *(cont.)*

Let's practice all the new letters we have learned (**n**, **m**, **h**, **r**, and **u**). Say the name of each letter as you write it.

n u

m r

h m

r u

Section 5

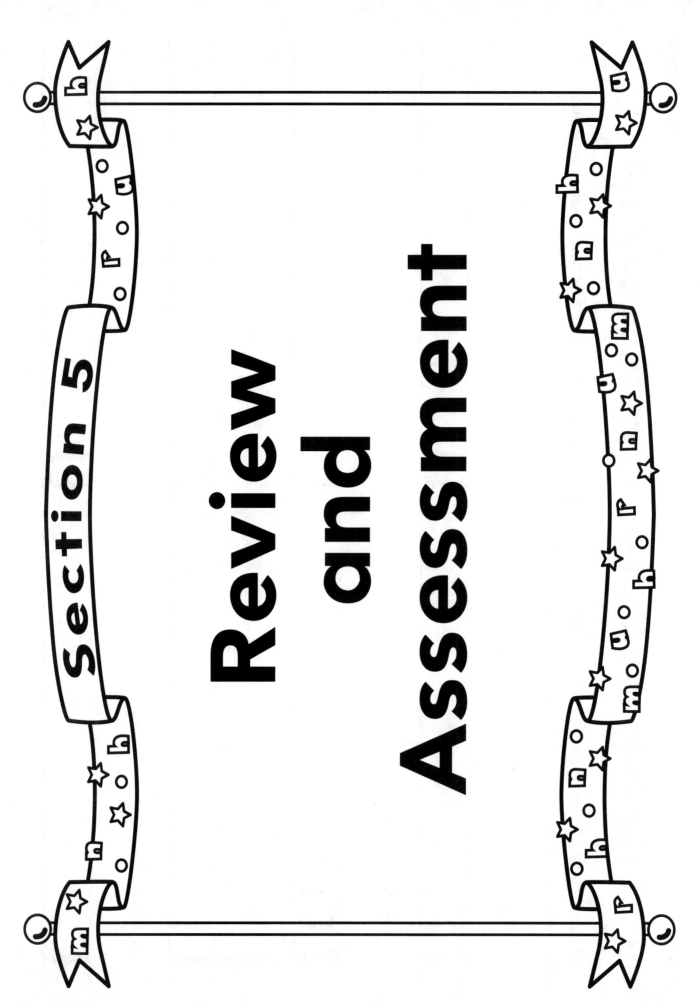

Review and Assessment

Cumulative Review and Assessment

You have learned all the letters of the alphabet! Here is a place to practice the last five letters you have learned. Say the name of each letter as you write it.

m	u
n	m
h	r
r	u

Cumulative Review and Assessment *(cont.)*

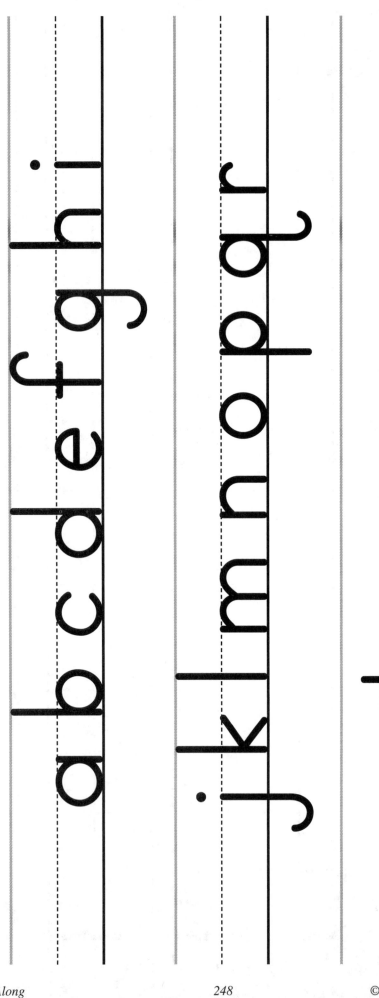

a b c d e f g h i

j k l m n o p q r

s t u v w x y z

Now you know all the letters of the alphabet! Let's review all of them. Remember to use our songs to help you remember how to write the letters.

Cumulative Review and Assessment *(cont.)*

Write these letters.

a a

b b

c c

d d

e e

f f

Cumulative Review and Assessment *(cont.)*

Write these letters.

g g j j

h h k k

i i l l

Cumulative Review and Assessment *(cont.)*

Write these letters.

m m

n n

o o

p p

q q

r r

Cumulative Review and Assessment *(cont.)*

Write these letters.

s s

v v

t t

w w

u u

x x

Cumulative Review and Assessment *(cont.)*

Write these letters.

y y

g h i j k l m

z z

n o p q r s

a b c d e f

t u v w x y z

Cumulative Review and Assessment *(cont.)*

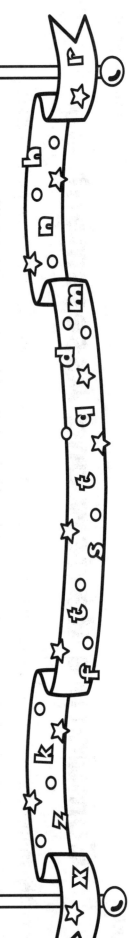

Look back over the letters you have written on pages 249–253. Those are all the letters that are in the alphabet, and you have written all of them!

Find the ones that you think look just as they should. Use a crayon to circle your best letters. Show them to your teacher.

Then go back and look at all your letters again. Are there any that need extra practice? If you see any that you want to practice some more before you are ready to show off, use some Ghost Paper (pages 260–285). Do not go on to the next part until you are happy with the way you write every letter!

Cumulative Review and Assessment *(cont.)*

Tani has written her last five letters here. She has left space for you to write your letters.

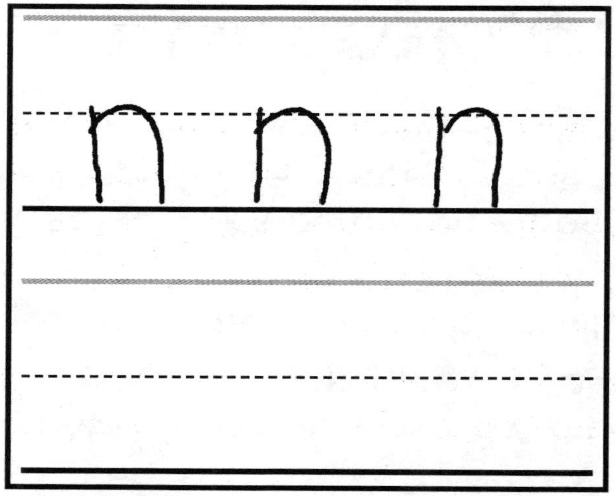

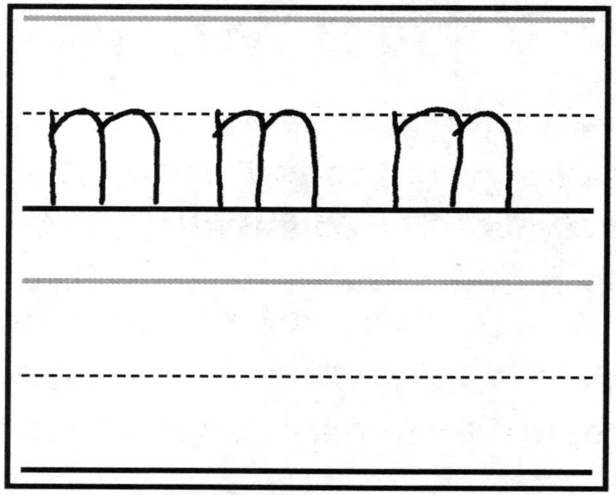

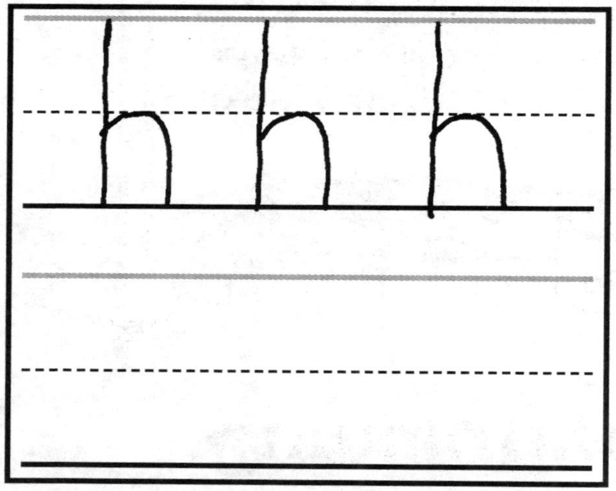

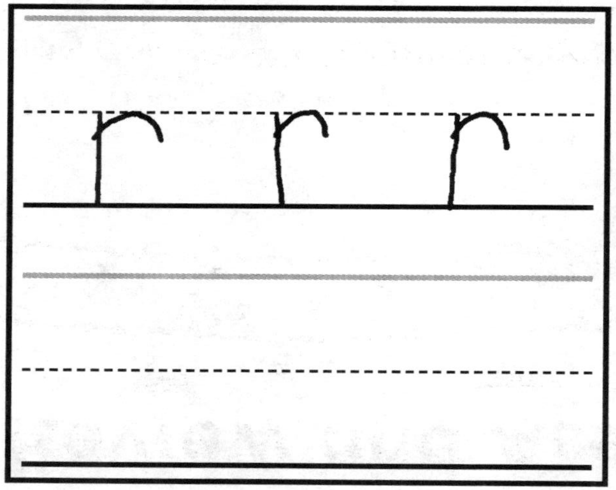

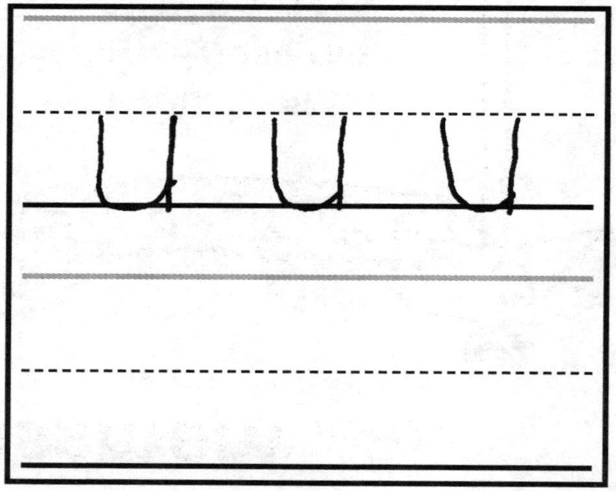

How do you think they look?

Cumulative Review and Assessment *(cont.)*

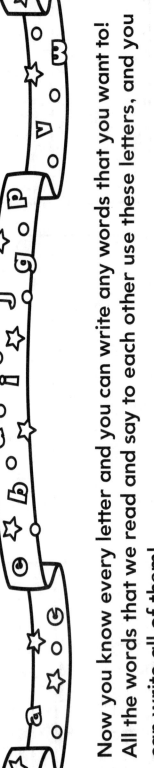

Now you know every letter and you can write any words that you want to! All the words that we read and say to each other use these letters, and you can write all of them!

The next two pages have words for you to write so that you can show how well you can make all the letters. Ask your teacher to read the words to you, and then write them as carefully and neatly as you can.

Use our songs to help you remember how to write the letters. Take your time, and do your very best.

Get ready to show off!

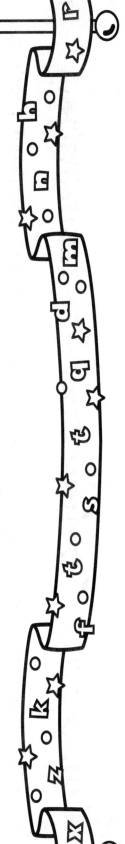

Cumulative Review and Assessment *(cont.)*

Write these words.

run	hat
axe	man
bow	very
zip	jar

Cumulative Review and Assessment *(cont.)*

Write these words.

zoo	flew
dug	jack
mop	quiz
slip	rope

Ghost Paper

Practice the Letter a

apple

ant

airplane

a a a a a a a a a

a a a a a a a a a

a a a a a a a a a

anchor

automobile

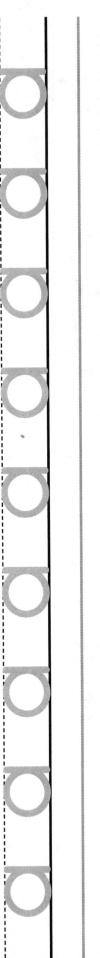

angel

Practice the Letter b

 ball  boat  bird

b b b b b b b b b b

b b b b b b b b b b

b b b b b b b b b b

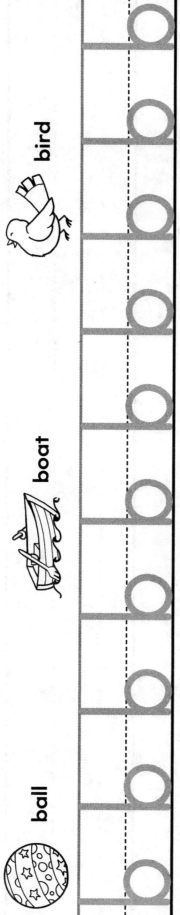

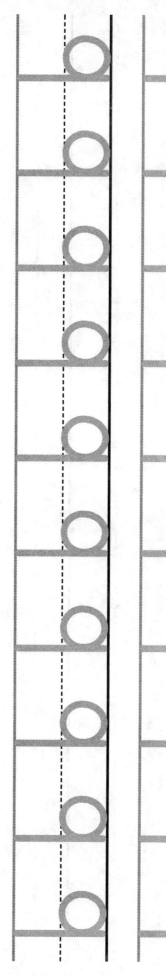

 barrel  book  bug

Practice the Letter c

 cat  cheese  crown

c c c c c c c c c c

c c c c c c c c c c

c c c c c c c c c c

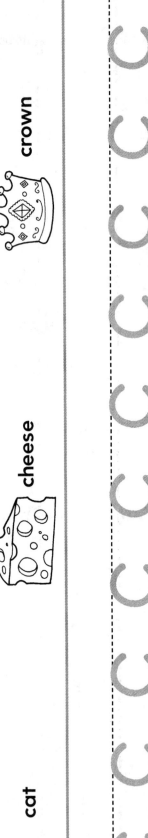

 city  clock 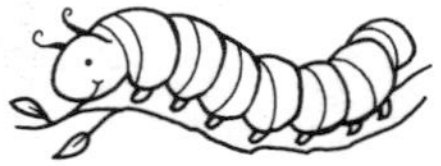 caterpillar

Practice the Letter d

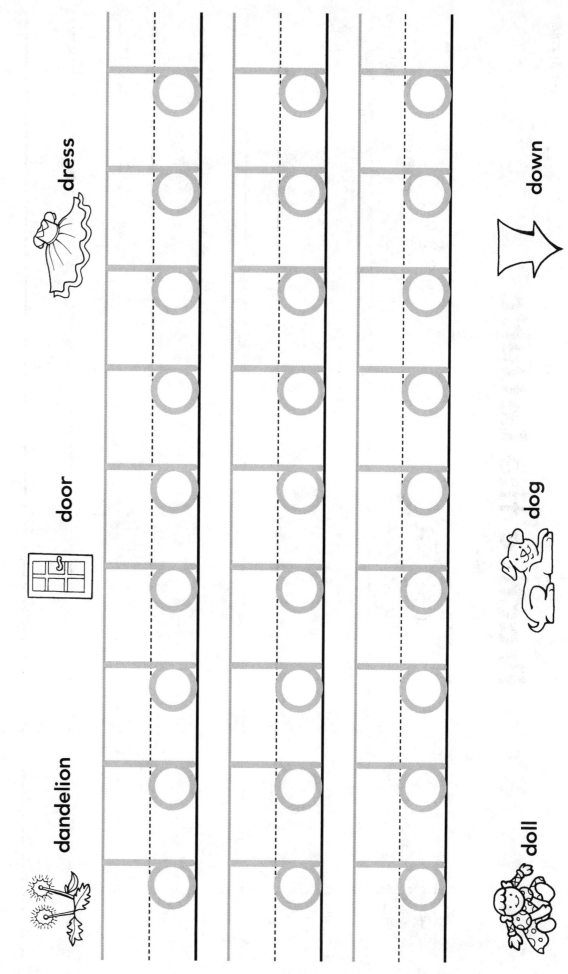

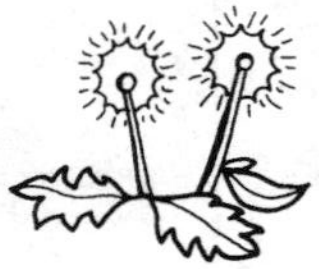 dandelion  door 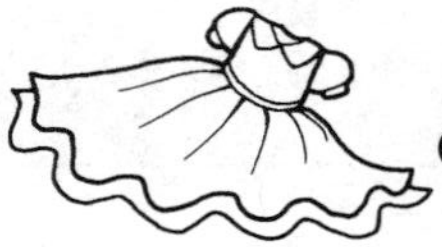 dress

d d d d d d d d d

d d d d d d d d d

d d d d d d d d d

 doll  dog 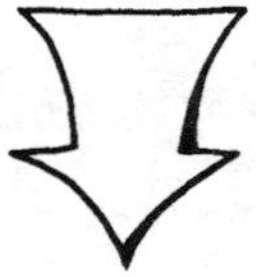 down

Practice the Letter e

 eye

 egg

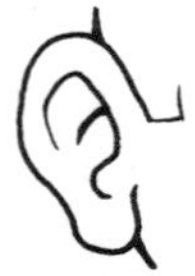 ear

e e e e e e e e e e

e e e e e e e e e e

e e e e e e e e e e

 elf

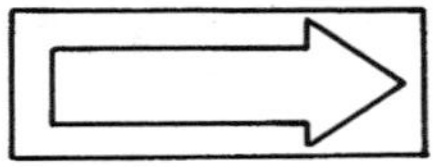 exit

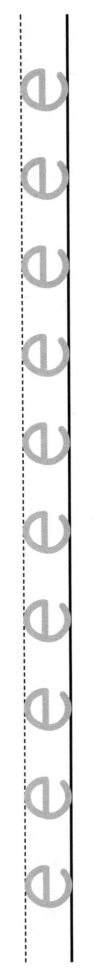

 elephant

Practice the Letter f

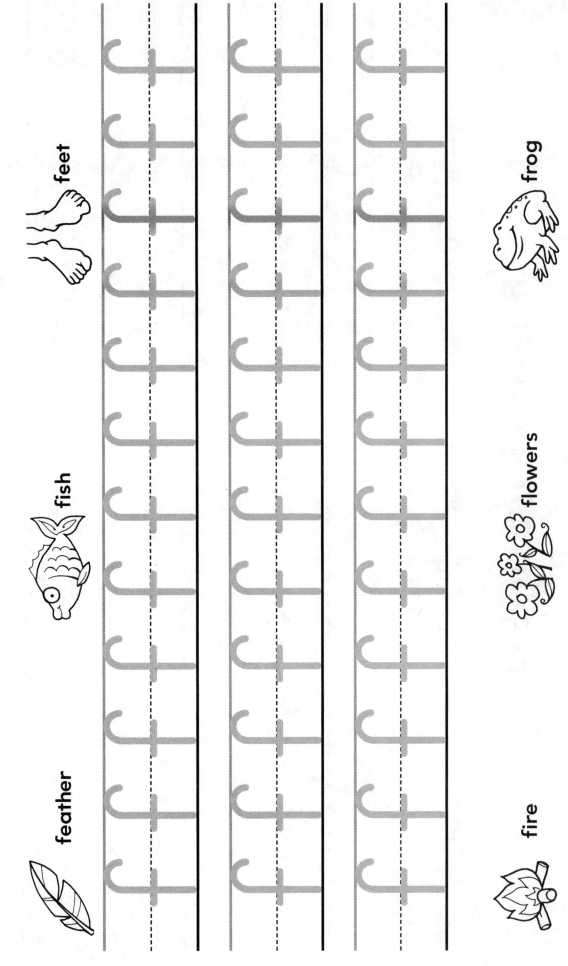

feather

fish

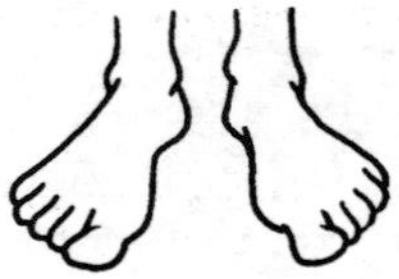
feet

f f f f f f f f f f f f

f f f f f f f f f f f f

f f f f f f f f f f f f

fire

flowers

frog

Practice the Letter g

 ghost  grapes  goose

g g g g g g g g g g

g g g g g g g g g g

g g g g g g g g g g

 grass 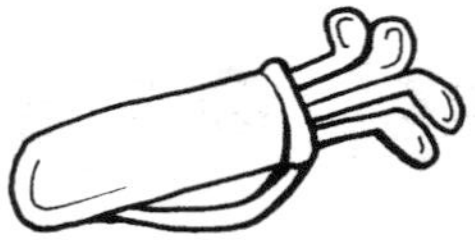 golf clubs  gear

Practice the Letter h

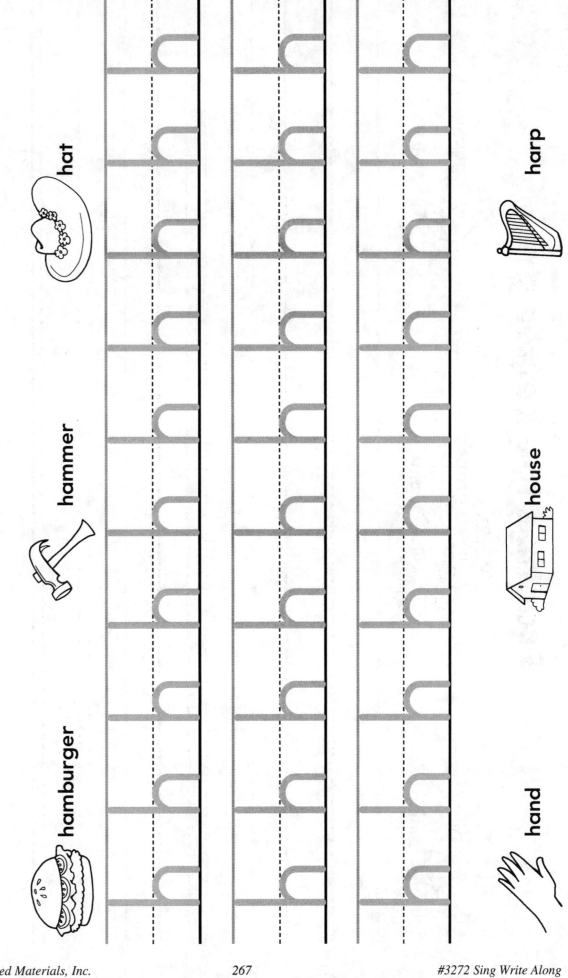

hamburger

hammer

hat

h h h h h h h h h h

h h h h h h h h h h

h h h h h h h h h h

hand

house

harp

Practice the Letter i

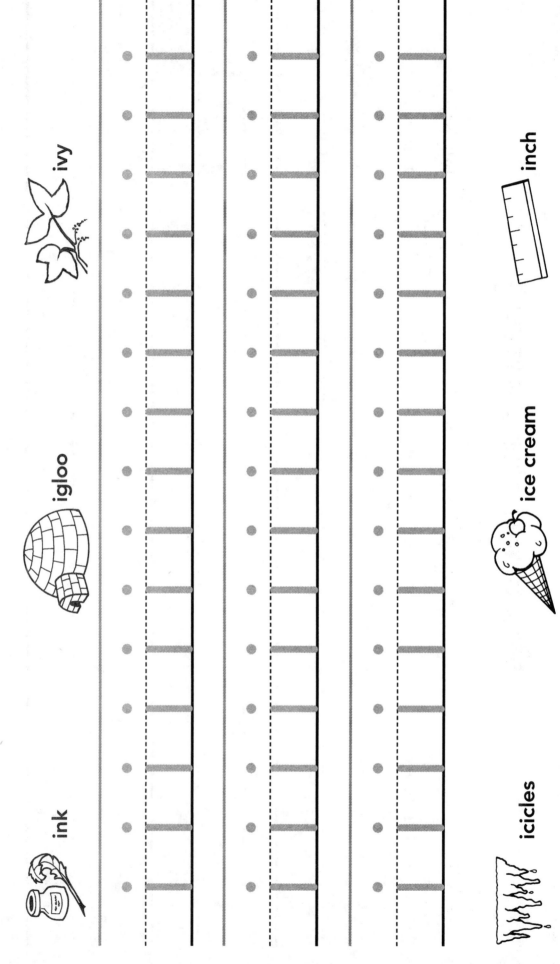

ink

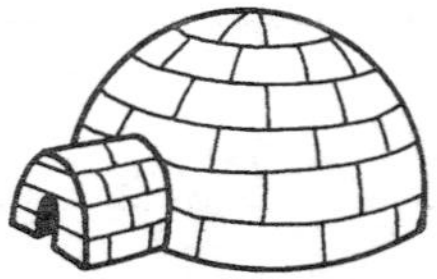
igloo

ivy

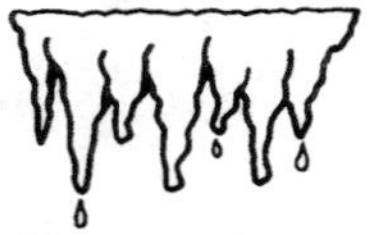
icicles

ice cream

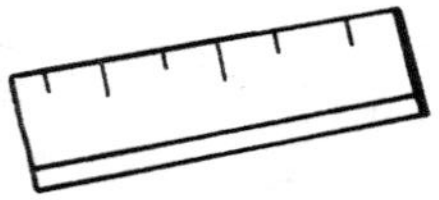
inch

Practice the Letter j

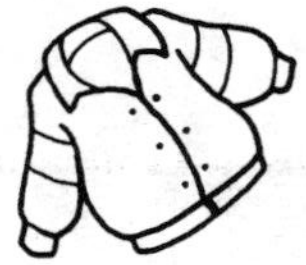 jacket  jack-in-the-box 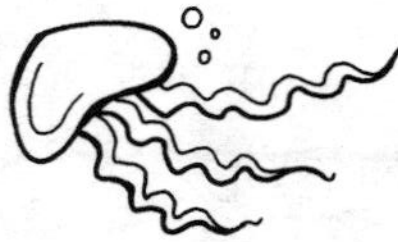 jellyfish

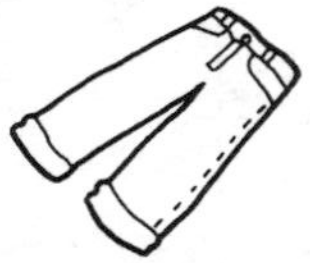 jeans  jar  jeep

Practice the Letter k

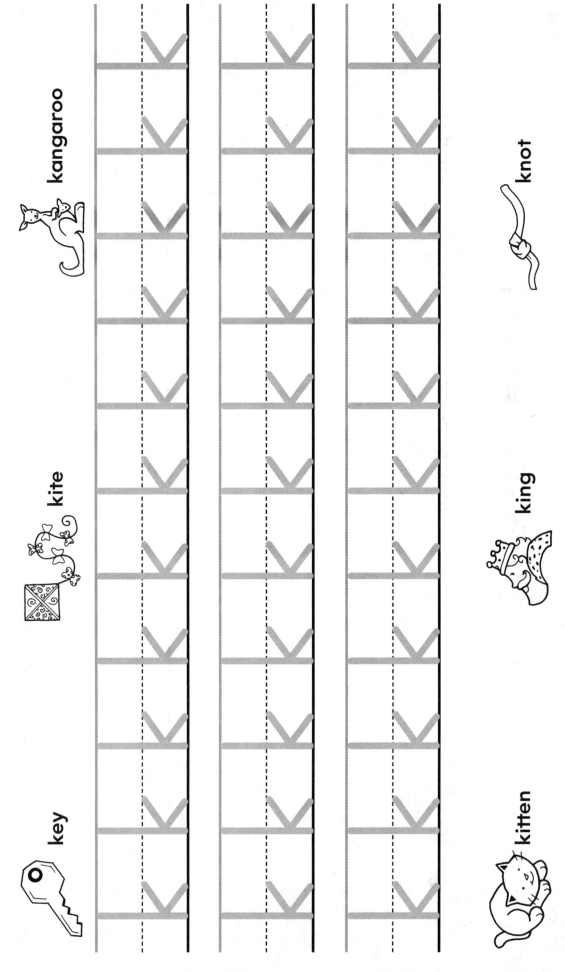

 key

 kite

 kangaroo

k k k k k k k k k k k

k k k k k k k k k k k

k k k k k k k k k k k

 kitten

 king

 knot

Practice the Letter l

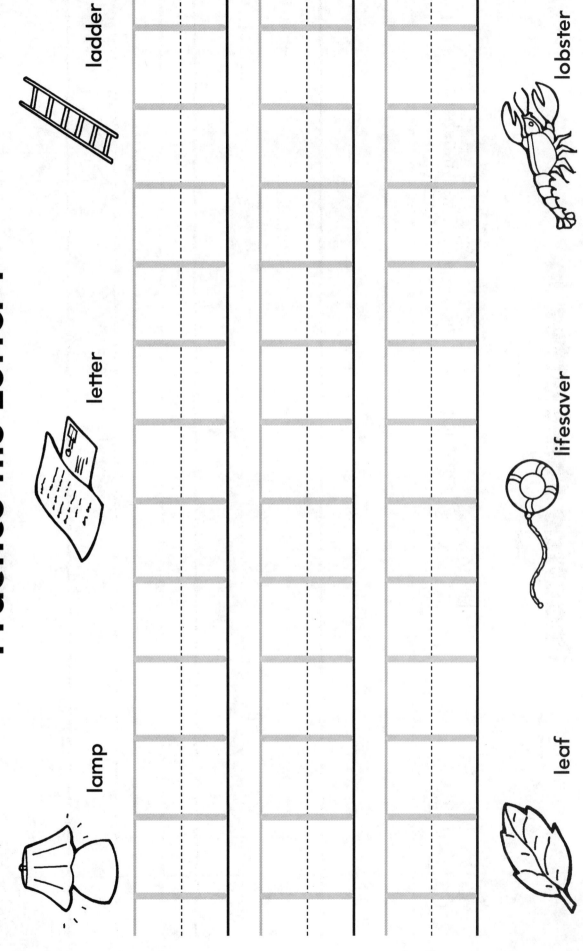

lamp

letter

ladder

leaf

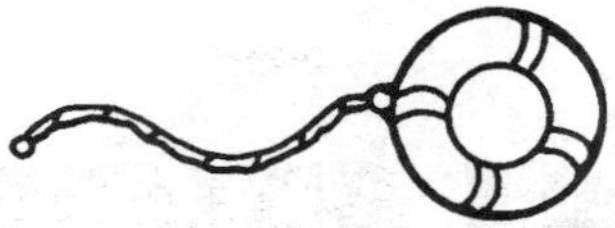
lifesaver

lobster

Practice the Letter m

 mouse  mustache  mushroom

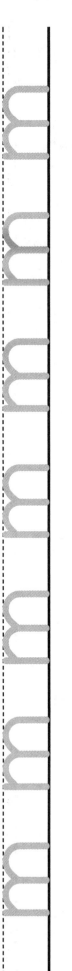

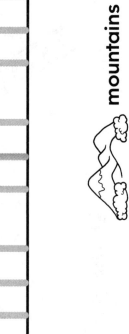

m m m m m m m

m m m m m m m

m m m m m m m

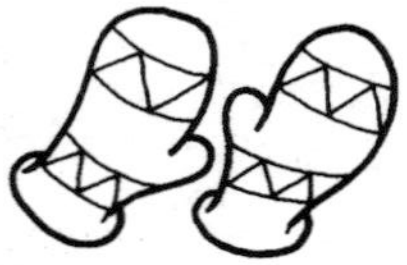 mittens  milk  mountains

Practice the Letter n

 nose 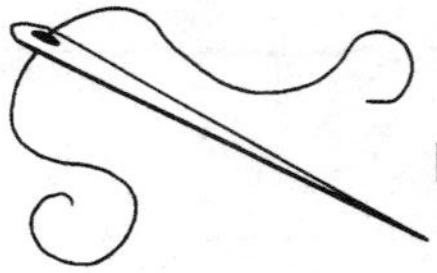 needle  nest

n n n n n n n n n n

n n n n n n n n n n

n n n n n n n n n n

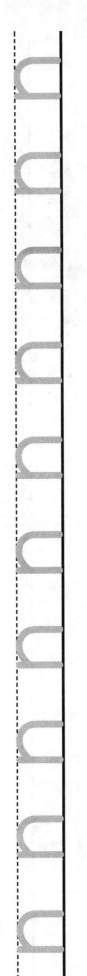

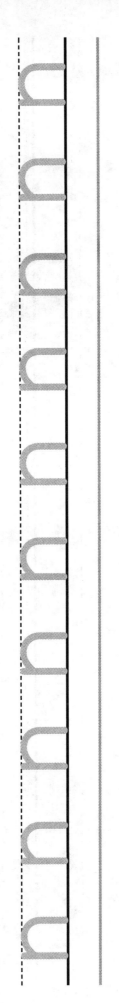

 nurse  necklace  night crawler

Practice the Letter o

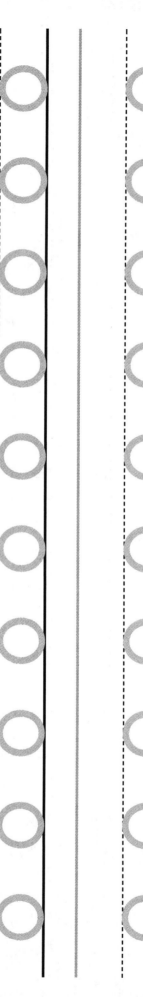

octopus

orange

owl

olives

one

onion

Practice the Letter p

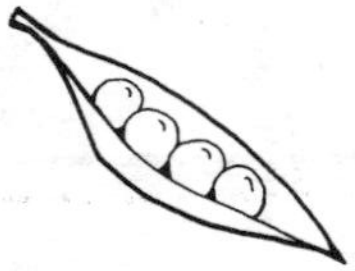 peas  pencil  pig

p p p p p p p p p p

p p p p p p p p p p

p p p p p p p p p p

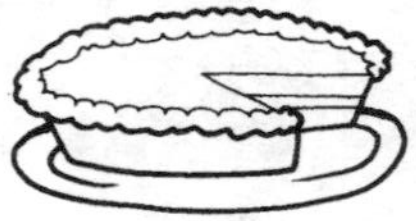 pie  pear  penguin

Practice the Letter q

 queen  quill  quarter

q q q q q q q q q q

q q q q q q q q q q

q q q q q q q q q q

 quail  question 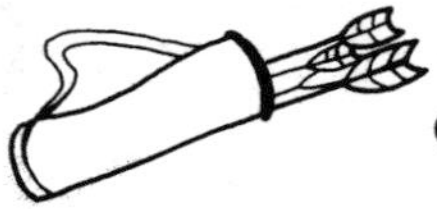 quiver

Practice the Letter r

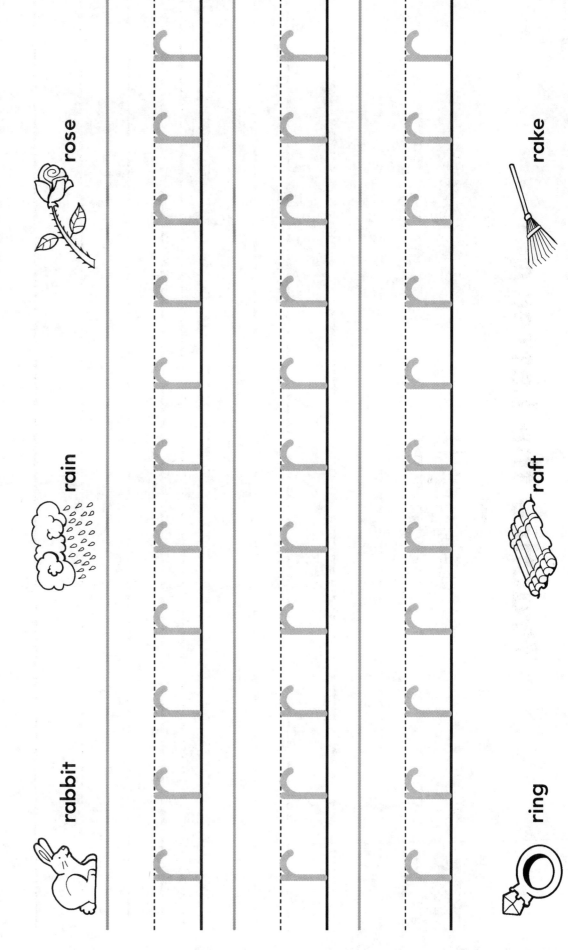

 rabbit  rain  rose

r r r r r r r r r r r

r r r r r r r r r r r

r r r r r r r r r r r

 ring  raft  rake

Practice the Letter s

 star  snake  snowman

s s s s s s s s s s s s

s s s s s s s s s s s s

s s s s s s s s s s s s

 shoe  spider  swan

Practice the Letter t

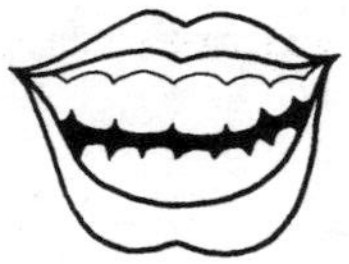 teeth  telephone  tacks

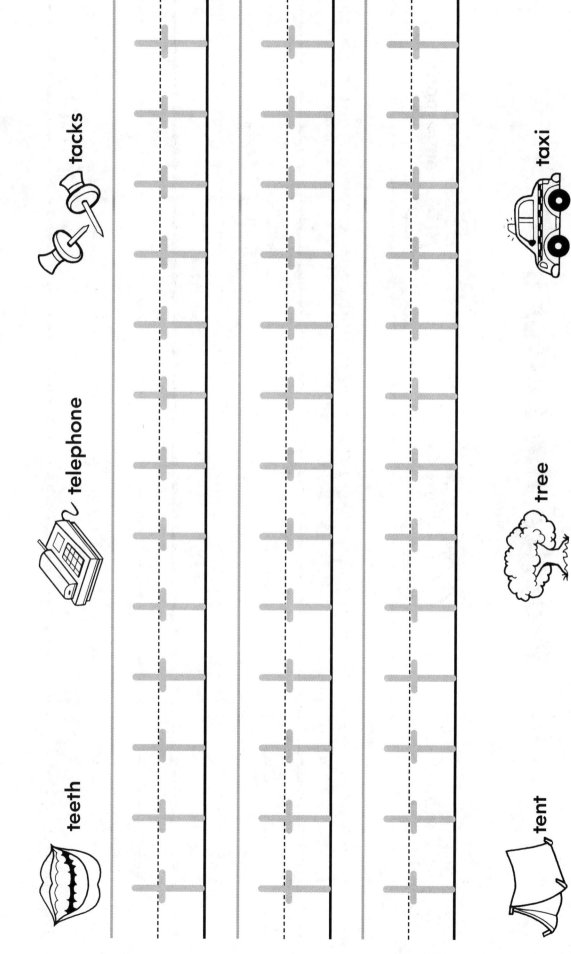

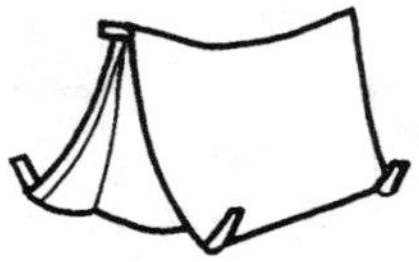 tent  tree  taxi

Practice the Letter u

 umbrella  urn  unicycle

u u u u u u u u u u

u u u u u u u u u u

u u u u u u u u u u

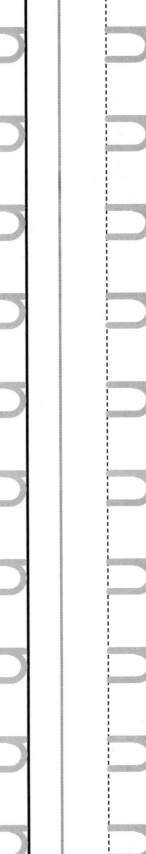

 unicorn  upside-down  umpire

Practice the Letter v

 valentine  vane  violin

v v v v v v v v v v v

v v v v v v v v v v v

v v v v v v v v v v v

 volcano  violet  vest

Practice the Letter w

 worm  waffle  wheel

w w w w w w w w

w w w w w w w w

w w w w w w w w

 windmill  wheelbarrow  wrench

Practice the Letter x

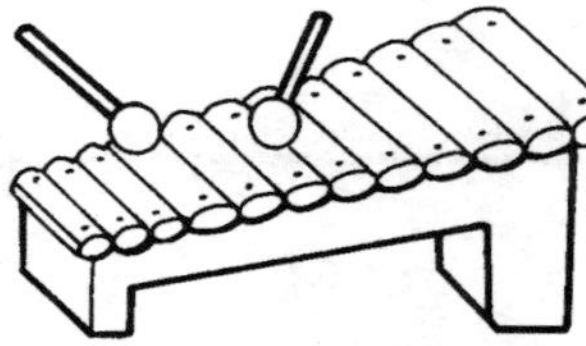
xylophone

railroad crossing

x x x x x x x x x x x

x x x x x x x x x x x

x x x x x x x x x x x

x-ray

x's for kisses

Practice the Letter y

yo-yo

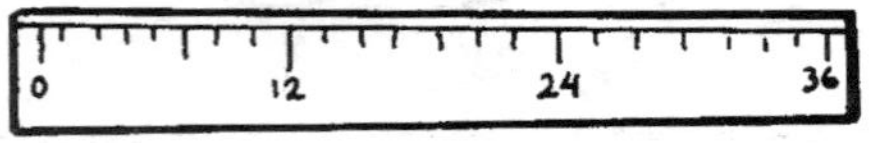

yardstick

yolk

yarn

Practice the Letter z

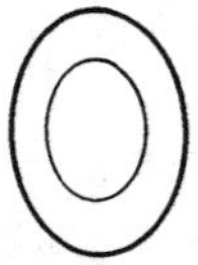
zero

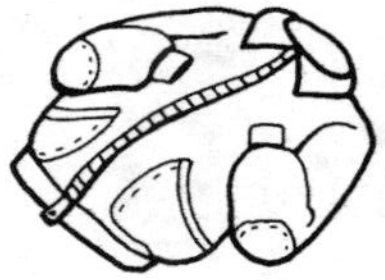
zipper

zinnias

zebra

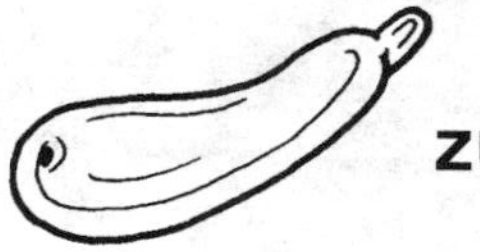
zucchini

zoo

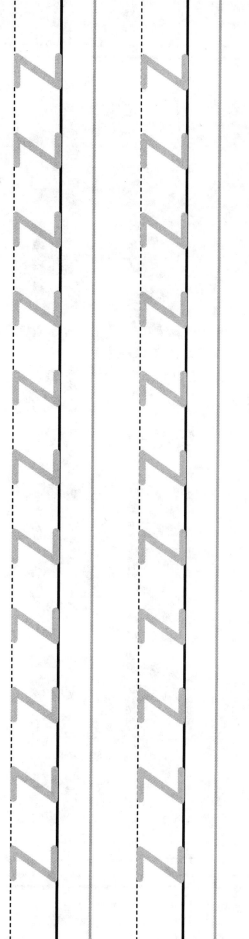

Section 7

Guide Paper and Certificate

Reproducible Guide Paper

Sing Write Along

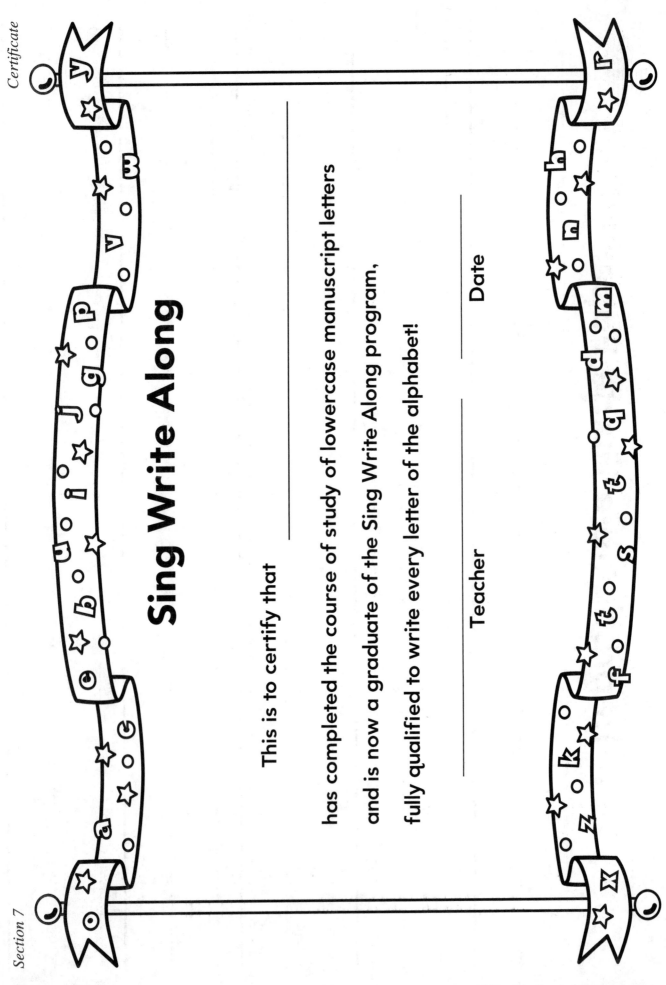

This is to certify that ______________________________

has completed the course of study of lowercase manuscript letters

and is now a graduate of the Sing Write Along program,

fully qualified to write every letter of the alphabet!

______________________________ ____________________

Teacher Date

